E L E C T R O N I C
S P R E A D S H E E T   A P P L I C A T I O N S
FOR
ACCOUNTING
PRINCIPLES

2d Edition

Includes Lotus® 1-2-3®
tutorial and
template diskette

Gaylord N. Smith, CPA
Professor
Albion College
Albion, Michigan

Copyright © 1990

by South-Western Publishing Co.

Cincinnati, Ohio

ISBN: 0-538-80534-X

Library of Congress Catalog Number: 89-63342

1 2 3 4 5 6 7 8 9 0 DH 6 5 4 3 2 1 0 9

Printed in the United States of America

Lotus and 1-2-3 are registered trademarks of Lotus Development Corporation.

Cover illustration by Lonnie Sue Johnson

AB81BB
PUBLISHED BY
SOUTH-WESTERN PUBLISHING CO.
CINCINNATI, OH   WEST CHICAGO, IL   DALLAS, TX   LIVERMORE, CA

PREFACE

Flexibility, power, and basic simplicity all combine to make spreadsheet programs very popular in today's business world. The most common uses of spreadsheet programs are for:

- financial planning and analysis
- preparation of financial statements, reports, and graphs
- performance of what-if analysis

In addition to these uses, there are many other applications for spreadsheet programs: depreciation schedules, budgets, tax planning and preparation, consolidations, statistical analysis, investment analysis, bookkeeping, etc.

The purpose of ELECTRONIC SPREADSHEET APPLICATIONS FOR ACCOUNTING PRINCIPLES is to bring this technology into the classroom. It is designed to allow accounting and finance students to learn the use of electronic spreadsheets along with their normal class assignments. Each workbook in the series contains more than 40 typical homework problems which have been restructured so that they can be solved using a spreadsheet program called Lotus® 1-2-3®[1]. The workbooks are generic in nature and may be used with any standard textbook in the field. A chart correlating problems in this workbook with several accounting principles texts is found on pages v-vi.

This workbook consists of a tutorial, sample problems, preprogrammed problems, model-building problems, and several appendices. The diskette which accompanies this workbook contains the files you will need for the tutorial and preprogrammed problems.

PREPROGRAMMED PROBLEMS

Problems are included for all the conceptual areas covered in accounting principles. Students develop formulas and enter data to complete partially preprogrammed templates. After the basic solution is developed, students perform what-if analyses and interpret graphical information. All preprogrammed problems have optional sections (called ticklers) that stretch the students' knowledge of Lotus 1-2-3 including:

- altering the physical appearance or components of the model
- creating and printing graphs
- writing macros

MODEL-BUILDING PROBLEMS

Short problems from a wide variety of accounting principles topics are provided to give students experience in developing their own models. Two sets of data are included for each problem so students can build the model with one set and test their model with the other. An optional section of each problem challenges students to create a graph from the data developed on the template.

TUTORIAL AND SAMPLE PROBLEMS

Many accounting principles students have been introduced to Lotus 1-2-3 in other classes, while many students are encountering the spreadsheet for the first time. ELECTRONIC SPREADSHEET APPLICATIONS FOR ACCOUNTING PRINCIPLES is structured for success for all students using the workbook.

A tutorial introduces the basics of running Lotus 1-2-3 on the IBM PC®[2] or IBM Personal System/2™[2]. It is not the purpose of this tutorial to teach extensive spreadsheet programming which typically requires at least 20 to 30 hours to learn. The tutorial contained in Lessons 1 through 5 takes about two hours to complete. It covers all the basic commands thoroughly, including graphing and macros, and introduces a few important frills.

The tutorial is designed for students who have never used a spreadsheet before, for students who are familiar with another spreadsheet and need to learn the Lotus 1-2-3 command structure, as well as students who need a refresher on Lotus 1-2-3.

The tutorial includes instructions for Versions 1A, 2.0, 2.01, and 2.2 of Lotus 1-2-3. The newer versions have several features not available on earlier versions, but the basics are very similar.

Sample Problems 1 through 5 introduce students to the methodology used in the workbook problems. Sample problems may be completed after the corresponding lesson in the tutorial, or they may be completed after the entire tutorial has been learned. Sample Problems 1 through 4 introduce the major sections of the preprogrammed problems. Sample Problem 5 should be completed before any of the model-building problems are attempted.

BENEFITS TO THE STUDENT

This series allows students to experience the excitement of working with the sophisticated software that is being used in the "real world." It is important to realize that this is not computer-assisted instruction in which the computer catches all the errors, does all the computations, and prints out the answer. Although every effort has been made to provide adequate guidance, it is up to the students to develop the final solutions and to tell the computer what to do. In completing these problems, students are stretching their knowledge of accounting principles concepts and learning to use a valuable software tool.

DISTINGUISHING FEATURES OF THIS WORKBOOK

The second edition of ELECTRONIC SPREADSHEET APPLICATIONS FOR ACCOUNTING PRINCIPLES builds on the success of the first edition in incorporating spreadsheet use as an integral part of the accounting principles curriculum. Among the advantages to instructors and students of using this workbook are:

1. **Variety of what-if analyses.** Solutions to textbook problems generally result in a single answer. Solving textbook problems with a pencil and paper is generally quicker than typing everything into a spreadsheet model. So why waste time and energy just for the thrill of using a spreadsheet program? The answer lies in the spreadsheet's ability to perform what-if analysis. All the problems in this workbook utilize the tremendous what-if capabilities of Lotus 1-2-3 to go beyond a single solution.

   After students develop the initial answer, they are asked a number of what-if questions. As a result, the spreadsheet models in the workbook are not only used to solve homework problems, they also reinforce the accounting concepts being taught in the classroom and they provide a demonstration of the instantaneous recalculative power of the spreadsheet program. As a result the computer's capabilities are being productively used by students.

2. **Use of graphics.** All problems in this workbook have optional graphics components. Students are asked to interpret graphs, to create graphs, to print graphs and to perform what-if graphing. Graphics is a rare feature in accounting spreadsheet material and this workbook pioneers this unique feature.

3. **Introduction of macros.** All problems in this workbook have optional macro components to introduce students to the very exciting world of programming Lotus 1-2-3. Students are given the opportunity of developing a variety of macros to print templates, save files, insert columns or rows, move portions of templates, and enter formulas. The design and creation of macros is another rare feature of accounting spreadsheet material.

4. **Classroom tested tutorial.** The basic 36 page tutorial introducing students to the world of Lotus 1-2-3 has been extensively classroom tested. Students are led through the Lotus 1-2-3 program in an efficient, step-by-step fashion. When students complete the tutorial, they will be prepared to work with existing models and to develop some reasonably sophisticated models of their own.

5. **Sound pedagogy.** In the design of the workbook, much attention has been given to enhancing the learning process, and supporting it. The learning process begins with a tutorial and sample problems which provide a sound foundation for completing the workbook problems. The preprogrammed problems require students to use accounting principles concepts to solve problems with partially completed models. Model-building problems challenge students to use accounting principles concepts and their knowledge of Lotus 1-2-3 to design their own models.

   Check figures are included for every problem. Appendices provide useful information including instructions for operating a microcomputer and ways to resolve problems.

INSTRUCTOR RESOURCES

Instructors adopting a workbook from this series will be provided with a solution disk and an instructor's manual. The disk contains solutions to all parts of the preprogrammed problems and suggested templates for the model-building problems. The manual has been reorganized for the second edition to improve the readability. For each problem, formulas and written answers required of students are provided first followed by all required printouts. The manual also contains suggestions on how to integrate the spreadsheet problems into the course, as well as other resource material.

ACKNOWLEDGEMENTS

I wish to thank several people who were involved in bringing this series to print: Ted Ricks for his enthusiastic and insightful leadership during the initial stage of this project; John Griffen for hours of technical assistance and for programming the demonstration diskette; and all the Albion College students who were so helpful in getting the first workbook completed. A very special thanks goes to current and former Albion College student Pamela Hamilton.

GAYLORD N. SMITH

CORRELATIONS OF PROBLEMS
WITH ACCOUNTING PRINCIPLES TEXTS

The following chart shows the correlation of the problems in this workbook with several accounting principles texts. The five texts shown in the correlation are:

Fess, Philip E. and Carl S. Warren. Accounting Principles, 16th ed. Cincinnati: South-Western Publishing Co., 1990.

Larson, Kermit D., and William W. Pyle. Fundamental Accounting Principles, 11th ed. Homewood, IL: Richard D. Irwin, Inc., 1987.

Meigs, Walter B., and Robert F. Meigs. Accounting: The Basis for Business Decisions, 8th ed. New York: McGraw-Hill Publishing Co., 1990.

Needles, Belverd E., Jr., Henry R. Anderson, and James C. Caldwell. Principles of Accounting, 3rd ed. Boston: Houghton Mifflin Company, 1987.

Walgenbach, Paul H., Ernest I. Hanson, and Norman E. Dittrich. Principles of Accounting, 4th ed. San Diego: Harcourt Brace Jovanovich, Publishers, 1987.

	Preprogrammed Problems	Fess	Larson	Meigs	Needles	Walgenbach
P1	Business Transactions	1	2	2	2	2
P2	Worksheet	3	4	4	4	4
P3	Merchandising Worksheet	4	5	5	5	5
P4	Merchandising Enterprise	5	5	5	5	5
P5	Purchases Journal	6	6	5	6	6
P6	Bank Reconciliation	7	7	7	7	7
P7	Discounted Notes Receivable	8	8	8	9	8
P8	Aging Accounts Receivable	8	8	8	9	8
P9	Gross Profit Method	9	9	9	10	9
P10	Depreciation	10	10	10	12	10
P11	Payroll Register	11	13	11	11	12
P12	Partnership	13	14	12	14	14
P13	Bond Pricing and Amortization	16	17	16	17	17
P14	Consolidations	17	16	17	20	18
P15	Statement of Cash Flow	18	18	19	18	19
P16	Ratio Analysis	19	20	20	19	20
P17	Manufacturing Accounting	20	21	21	22	21
P18	Process Costing	22	22	22	24	23
P19	Cost-Volume-Profit Analysis	23	24	23	25	24
P20	Variable Costing	24	24	23	25	25
P21	Master Budget	25	25	25	26	26
P22	Flexible Budgeting	25	26	25	27	26
P23	Material and Labor Variances	25	26	25	27	26
P24	Departmental Income Statement	26	23	24	25	25
P25	Capital Budgeting	28	27	26	28	27

NC - Topic not covered in text.

TABLE OF CONTENTS

LOTUS 1-2-3 TUTORIAL

The first section of this workbook, the Lotus 1-2-3 tutorial, consists of five lessons that are designed to acquaint you with the Lotus 1-2-3 program. This tutorial is not written to teach you in-depth Lotus 1-2-3 programming. Its purpose is to expose you to the basic elements of 1-2-3 and prepare you to solve the problems in this workbook. You are strongly encouraged to explore more advanced 1-2-3 programming on your own after completing this tutorial. You can learn about 1-2-3 in more detail from the Lotus 1-2-3 manual that accompanies the Lotus 1-2-3 program. There are numerous reference materials available on 1-2-3 in many bookstores and computer stores.

Lotus 1-2-3 is called an electronic spreadsheet. What exactly is an electronic spreadsheet? Imagine a large sheet of accounting paper with many columns and rows. In the business world, this is often referred to as a worksheet or spreadsheet. Spreadsheets are commonly used to gather financial data and to accumulate the results. Electronic spreadsheets are computer programs that are similar to paper spreadsheets in structure and format. One big difference with electronic spreadsheets is that the columns and rows appear on a computer screen rather than on paper. Another difference is that spreadsheet calculations can be performed by the computer instead of manually. This tutorial is designed to explain exactly how Lotus 1-2-3 works.

If you are not already familiar with using a microcomputer, turn to Appendix A in this workbook before beginning Lesson 1. This appendix contains brief instructions on running the IBM PC, and on the care and handling of disks.

LESSON 1

BASIC USER SKILLS

Learning Objectives

Topics introduced in this lesson are:

- loading Lotus 1-2-3 into the computer
- moving the cursor around the worksheet
- entering labels and data, including editing techniques
- using the Undo command (Version 2.2 only)
- using Lotus 1-2-3 to perform arithmetic calculations
- designing Lotus 1-2-3 formulas
- using the @SUM special summation function
- retrieving and saving files (File Retrieve and File Save)
- performing what-if analysis
- using the Range Erase, File Erase, and Worksheet Erase commands
- printing files including compressed mode (Print commands)
- formatting and preparing a new file disk

LOADING LOTUS 1-2-3 INTO THE COMPUTER

Before beginning this lesson, you should have the Lotus 1-2-3 System Disk and an IBM PC DOS or MS DOS disk (2.0 or higher)[1]. These disks must be obtained from your instructor. You must also have the Template Disk which is included in the workbook you purchased. Insert the DOS disk into disk drive A and turn on the computer. The red light on the drive will go on and then will go out again. If requested by your computer, enter the date and then the time, pressing ENTER (↵) after each entry. In a few more seconds, you will see the operating system prompt. This manual uses A> to represent the operating system prompt, but your prompt may look different. Remove the DOS disk,

---

[1] If you are using a computer with a hard disk, check with your instructor for directions on loading Lotus 1-2-3.

insert the Lotus 1-2-3 System Disk in drive A and the Template Disk in drive B. Type **LOTUS** and press ENTER. (You may use either capital or lower-case letters. The commands that you are to enter from the keyboard are indicated in bold type in this tutorial.) Shortly, you will see the first Lotus 1-2-3 screen. The heading will indicate that this is the 1-2-3 Access System.

In the heading you will see several words such as 1-2-3, PrintGraph, Translate, and so forth. Each of these represents an activity category that can be accessed by the Lotus 1-2-3 program. The only one you will be concerned with now is 1-2-3. Press ENTER now, and 1-2-3 will be loaded. With Version 1A, you will need to press one more key before the program will be ready to run. The computer monitor will appear as shown in Illustration 1.

If the program does not load properly, check to make sure that you have inserted the Lotus 1-2-3 System Disk and not another disk into the drive. After checking this, repeat the procedure described above. If you still have difficulty getting the program to load properly, contact your instructor.

After the program is loaded, leave the 1-2-3 System Disk in the drive. There are occasions when it

may be needed while you are working with the program.

ESCAPE or CONTROL BREAK

As you work through this tutorial, you will frequently be asked to enter commands into the computer using various keys on the keyboard. Occasionally, you may make a mistake by pressing the wrong key. When this occurs, you can use the ESCAPE (ESC) key to "escape" from the incorrect entry. Pressing the ESC key once or twice will eliminate the error and get you back to the READY mode (see the upper right corner of the screen). This will allow you to start over with the proper entry.

With some commands, you may have to press ESC several times. A quicker way to completely delete a long command that has been entered is to press the CONTROL (CTRL) key and the BREAK key at the same time. (See the keyboard illustrations in Appendix A if you need help locating these keys.) Pressing these two keys at the same time will delete any commands currently entered.

Illustration 1
Lotus 1-2-3 Screen Display

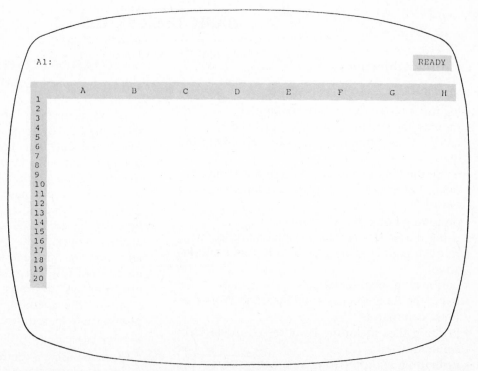

1-2-3 COMMANDS

The 1-2-3 program contains commands that help manipulate the spreadsheet. These commands can only be entered when the program is in the READY mode. Press the Slash (/) key (not the Backslash (\) key). A menu appears at the top of the screen in the Control Panel.

Each word on the upper line of the menu stands for a different command, as the table below indicates.

Worksheet	General commands affecting the whole worksheet
Range	Commands affecting specific portions of the worksheet
Copy	Copy a cell or range of cells
Move	Move a cell or range of cells
File	Commands affecting files saved on a storage disk
Print	Print a worksheet
Graph	Graphical display of worksheet data
Data	Special data manipulation commands
System	Exit to DOS (not available in Version 1A)
Add-In	Allows access to programs written by developers (Version 2.2 only)
Quit	End 1-2-3 session; exit to Lotus Access System Menu

All of the 1-2-3 commands that are pertinent to the problems in the workbook will be introduced in this tutorial. Press ESC now to clear the menu.

HELP Key (F1)

1-2-3 uses the function key marked F1 as a HELP key. (Refer to the keyboard illustrations in Appendix A if you need help locating the function keys.) Any time you have questions on the particular command you are entering, press the F1 key. Immediately the screen will fill with instructions and information. Use the arrow keys to maneuver around the HELP screen. Try the F1 key now if you wish. With Version 2.2, the Help program has been placed on a separate Help Disk which you must insert in drive A before the F1 key is pressed. Press ESC to get back to the worksheet when done. (Warning: If you are using someone else's copy of Lotus 1-2-3, do not be surprised if the HELP key (F1) doesn't work. The owners of the Lotus 1-2-3 disks frequently delete the Help program from the Lotus 1-2-3 System Disk to create more room to store other programs.)

CURSOR MOVEMENT—ARROW KEYS

Notice that the screen is mostly blank but that there is a row of numbers down the side and letters in sequence (A, B, C, etc.) across the top. These numbers and letters frame the worksheet section of the program.

Arrow keys are on the right side of the keyboard under the numbers 2, 4, 6, and 8. Now, while watching the screen, press the Right Arrow key on the keyboard. If you hear a short buzz, the program is telling you that you don't know your right from your left!

When the Right Arrow key is pressed once, the highlighted, rectangular box shifts over to a position under the B column. This highlighted box is known as the cursor (sometimes referred to as the cell pointer).

The area above the worksheet is called the Control Panel. Notice that there is a B1 in the upper left corner of the Control Panel. This indicates the position of the cursor on the worksheet. The letter "B" indicates the column, and the number "1" indicates the row. Now use the Left Arrow key to move the cursor back to cell A1 and notice that the symbol in the Control Panel changes back to A1. The cursor indicates the position of the "active cell."

Now for one of the surprises of this program. Press the Right Arrow key repeatedly until the cursor moves past the last column shown on the right side of the screen. Note that new columns appear in alphabetic sequence. This is called scrolling. You can speed up the cursor movement by pressing the Right Arrow key and holding it down. If the computer starts to beep at you, take your finger off the Right Arrow key momentarily to allow the cursor to catch up. The far right column is "IV." That's 256 columns!

1-2-3 also has more rows than are shown on the screen. Scroll the cursor downward and notice the row numbers change as you move the cursor past the last row shown on the screen. Stop when you get to row 100. It would take a long time for you to find the bottom of the worksheet since it is 8,192 rows deep! (Version 1A has 2048 rows and the Student Edition contains 64 columns and 256 rows.)

As you can see, the worksheet is very large. There are over two million cells that can be accessed. (Version 1A is limited to about half a million cells.) What shows on the screen is only a small portion of the entire area. The computer screen can be thought of as a window for viewing a small portion of the entire worksheet.

OTHER METHODS OF CURSOR MOVEMENT

There are several ways to quickly move the cursor around the worksheet that are particularly helpful for long distances. One method is to use the function key marked F5. Press that key now. Remember, if you enter something incorrectly, use the ESC key. Notice the following message in the Control Panel:

Enter address to go to: xxxx

Ignore the cell reference (xxxx) for now. You are being asked to enter the particular location that you wish to move to. Type **A1** (either capital or lowercase letters may be used) and press the ENTER key. Bingo! The cursor will immediately move to cell A1.

Another way to move the cursor is to use the keys marked PAGE UP (PG UP) and PAGE DOWN (PG DN). Press the PG DN key and watch what happens. This command moves the screen down 20 lines on the worksheet (a page). The PG UP key moves the screen up 20 lines. The TAB (↔) key does the same thing, moving the screen left and right. Use the SHIFT key with the TAB key to move the screen to the left. Go ahead and experiment with these four keys.

A third way to move long distances quickly is to use the END key. Regardless of where the cursor is now, press the END key once and then the Right Arrow key once. What happens? As you can see, the END key/Arrow key combination moves the cursor to the END of the row or column that the cursor is on. (The cursor will stop if it bumps into a cell that isn't empty.) Practice using the END key a while. See if you can get the cursor positioned in the lower right corner of the worksheet.

There is a fourth method that should also be mentioned here. Press the HOME key and watch what happens. The HOME key always moves the cursor to cell A1. This is a rather limited, but very helpful, key.

DATA ENTRY AND EDITING

You are ready to begin learning how to enter data on the spreadsheet and how to edit cell contents. There are two categories of data that may be entered on a spreadsheet: labels and values. The editing features of a spreadsheet allow you to make corrections and changes to these data.

Labels and Values

Labels are letters or words that are placed on a spreadsheet. With the cursor positioned in cell A1, type the word **COMPUTER**. Remember to use the ESC key if you make an error. You may use either capital or lowercase letters. Note that as soon as you type the letter C, the word LABEL appears in the Mode Indicator on the right side of the Control Panel.

Input is not actually stored in the cell until the ENTER key (or one of the arrow keys) is pressed. Pressing one of the arrow keys serves the dual purpose of storing input in a cell and moving the cursor in the direction of the arrow. This is particularly helpful when entering a large amount of data in a row or column. Press the ENTER key or one of the arrow keys now. This action stores the label COMPUTER in cell A1.

Now position the cursor in cell A5, type your full name, and press ENTER. What happens? You will undoubtedly find that your name does not all fit in one cell. In fact, each cell holds only nine characters. If your label is longer than nine characters, it bleeds over to the next cell (as long as that cell is empty).

Move the cursor to cell G1, type the word **DOG**, and press ENTER. Now move the cursor to cell F1, type the words **PERSONAL COMPUTER**, and press ENTER. From the result, you can see that you must be careful when entering labels that bleed over to other cells.

Values are cell inputs that are either numbers or formulas. On the IBM PC, you may use either the number keys across the top of the keyboard or those on the keypad on the right side of the keyboard. To use the numbers on the keypad, press the NUM LOCK key once. This turns the numbers "on." To get the arrow keys again, press the NUM LOCK key once more to turn the numbers "off." For this tutorial, do not use the number keys from the keypad since you need to use these keys as arrow keys.

Move the cursor to cell D11. Type the number **123** using the number keys across the top of the keyboard. As soon as the 1 is typed, note that the word VALUE appears in the Mode Indicator. Now press ENTER. The value 123 is now stored in cell D11.

The 1-2-3 program identifies your cell input as either a label or a value by the first character you enter in the cell. If the first character is a letter, the word LABEL appears in the Mode Indicator. If it is a number, the word VALUE appears.

Now that you are familiar with entering values, let's try a simple exercise. In cell A6 (right under your name), enter your home street address (for example: 27495 Short Street) and press ENTER. What happens? The program does not let you enter your address in the cell. In fact, as you can see by the Mode Indicator, you are now in the EDIT mode which means something has to be changed. The lesson here is that you cannot mix values and labels in the same cell. However, it is possible to enter numbers in a cell as a part of a label. To demonstrate this, you first have to get out of the EDIT mode. Press the ESC key twice to eliminate your address and get you out of the EDIT mode.

Now let's start over. With the cursor in cell A6, press the Apostrophe (') key. It is right under the Quotation Mark (") on the same key. Be careful; don't use the Accent (`) key which is right next door on some keyboards. The apostrophe triggers the 1-2-3 program to expect a label, as the Mode Indicator now shows. Now type your address and press ENTER. Your address should appear beginning in cell A6. The apostrophe should not show in the cell. You will need to use this technique every time you wish to enter a label in which the first character is a number.

Editing Cell Contents

If you make a typing error that you catch before you press the ENTER key, you may make a correction immediately by using the BACKSPACE (←) key. Each time you press the BACKSPACE key, a letter or digit is deleted. Move the cursor to cell B1, type **COMPTER** (but do not press ENTER), and then use the BACKSPACE key to eliminate the three incorrect letters (TER) and type the correct ones (**UTER**). Press ENTER when the word has been corrected.

The ESC key may also be used to correct an error you catch before pressing ENTER. Pressing the ESC key will delete the whole entry. Move the cursor to cell C1, type the number **456**, but don't press ENTER. Now press the ESC key and watch the whole number be deleted.

If you make a typing error that you catch after you press ENTER, you may make a correction using the key marked F2. To demonstrate this, move the cursor to cell C3, type the word **MACRO**, and press ENTER. Now let's change this word to MICRO. Press the F2 key. Use the Left Arrow key to position the blinking edit cursor under the letter to be deleted (the A in this case). Next, press the

DELETE (DEL) key to delete the letter A. Then type the correct letter (an **I**) and press ENTER. When you press ENTER, the correction will appear on the screen in cell C3.

If you wish to rewrite a cell's contents totally, simply position the cursor in that cell, type over what is already in the cell, and press ENTER. Let's try that now by changing the entry in cell A1 from COMPUTER to LOTUS. Move the cursor to cell A1, type the word **LOTUS**, and press ENTER. You can see that the word LOTUS replaces the word COMPUTER in cell A1. This is a quick way to change short labels or values.

Move the cursor to cell G3, type the words **PERSONAL COMPUTER**, and press ENTER. Suppose you now wish to erase the word COMPUTER. Even though it appears that you should move to cell H3 to erase that word, that won't work because the word COMPUTER is really in cell G3. It bleeds into cell H3 when shown on the screen, but it is actually entered in cell G3. With the cursor still in cell G3, press the Edit key (F2) and then the BACKSPACE key several times to eliminate the word COMPUTER. Press ENTER when done.

Range Erase

Once you have typed a label or a value in a cell and have pressed the ENTER key to store it in the cell, you may use the Edit key (F2) and the BACKSPACE key to completely erase the contents of the cell. Another way to completely erase the contents of a cell is to use the Range Erase command.

Range Erase is one of the commands that is activated by the Slash key. To demonstrate this command, move the cursor to cell A1. Once there, check to make sure you are in the READY mode, then press the Slash key to see the menu of commands. Notice that the word "Worksheet" in the menu is highlighted. This highlighted box is called the menu pointer. The Left and Right Arrow keys are used to move the menu pointer to the desired command. Press the Right Arrow key to move the menu pointer to the word "Range." Notice that the words on the line under the main menu change as you move the menu pointer. The second line shows the description or subcommands that apply to the highlighted command. Use the arrow keys now to move the menu pointer across the top of the screen and check the subcommands and descriptions shown for each command.

Now let's locate the specific command to erase the contents of a cell. As mentioned previously, the command category "Range" contains commands that affect specific portions of the worksheet. A range may be one cell, one or more rows, one or more columns, or a block of cells. Since you do not want to erase the whole worksheet, you will begin with the Range command. Move the menu pointer to Range and press ENTER to select this command. Remember to use the ESC key or the CTRL and BREAK keys if you make any erroneous keystrokes.

Once you have selected the command, you are presented with a menu of subcommands which are listed below. On Version 1A the word Label is shown as Label-Prefix. With Version 2.2, the menu also includes Search.

> Format
> Label
> Erase
> Name
> Justify
> Protect
> Unprotect
> Input
> Value
> Transpose

Now you must select the subcommand that will erase a cell. Press the Right Arrow key two times to move the menu pointer to the word "Erase" and press ENTER to select this subcommand.

Above the worksheet you now see the following:

> Enter range to erase: A1..A1

You can respond in one of four ways: press ENTER to accept the computer's suggestion; use the arrow keys to enter your own range (called "pointing"); type the beginning and ending cell references to specify the range; or press ESC to stop and back up or CTRL BREAK to stop the command completely. Each of these options may be used whenever the 1-2-3 program asks you to specify a range of cells. A discussion of the first three options, with an example of each, follows. The fourth option, to use the ESC or CTRL BREAK keys, was discussed previously.

1. By pressing ENTER now, you can accept the program's suggested range, which is a single cell (A1). Press ENTER now and you should find that the word LOTUS disappears from cell A1.
2. By using the arrow keys, you can point to a range of cells beginning with the current cursor position and ending with the cell to which the cursor is moved. To demonstrate the pointing

technique, position the cursor in cell B1 and enter the Range Erase command again beginning with the Slash key. (Shortcut: Simply type the keys /RE rather than using the arrow keys to point to the commands.) Now, in response to "Enter range to erase: B1..B1," press the Right Arrow key once. Notice that the cursor moves to cell C1 and that the range is now B1..C1. Press the Down Arrow key twice (B1..C3). As you can see, this causes the range to expand into a rectangular shape (B1..C3). Press ENTER and notice all cell contents in the range are erased.
3. You may also specify a range by typing the beginning (upper left) and ending (lower right) cell references. For example, enter the Range Erase command again (/RE). Then type **F1.G3** and press ENTER. All the cells in that range are now erased.

As mentioned previously, 1-2-3 commands can only be executed with the program in the READY mode. It is easy to forget this. To demonstrate a common error, move the cursor to cell B17, type **PLAY**, and do not press ENTER. Suppose you now decide to erase this word. Press the Slash key to begin the Range Erase command. Why doesn't the menu appear in the Control Panel? The menu does not appear because the program accepted the Slash key as a label rather than as a command. (Note that the Mode Indicator says LABEL.) Press ENTER now to store PLAY/ in B17. Now the program will be in the READY mode and will accept commands. With the cursor still in cell B17, enter the /Range Erase command again (/RE) and press ENTER. The contents of cell B17 is now erased.

Using the Undo Feature (Version 2.2 only)

When you are in the READY Mode, Version 2.2 allows you to reverse or cancel the last thing you did. For example, the last steps you performed were to erase PLAY/ from cell B17. Suppose you now decide you want PLAY/ in cell B17. To undo you erasure, hold down the ALT key and press the F4 key once. You notice now that PLAY/ reappears in cell B17. The undo feature is very helpful for recovering from mistakes. It can only be used to undo the last 1-2-3 command sequence entered.

Arithmetic Calculations

The basic mathematical operations that 1-2-3 can perform are addition, subtraction, multiplication, division, and exponentiation. There are also more complex mathematical functions that 1-2-3 can perform. Some of these special function commands are mentioned below, and many are discussed in detail in Appendix C.

The table at the bottom of the page indicates the keyboard keys for each mathematical operation.

You will find all of the operator keys on the keyboard, some in more than one place. The Caret (^) key is above the number 6 key on a standard IBM PC keyboard. Let's try the addition example now. Remember to use the BACKSPACE and ESC keys to correct errors. Move the cursor to cell D12, type **123+456**, and press ENTER. Immediately in the cell you will see the answer 579. Use cell D12 to try the other examples shown in the table above and check your answers. Remember to press ENTER after typing each example.

It is also possible to perform several mathematical operations at once. For example, the following is a perfectly acceptable formula to enter in a cell: **4+6/2-1**. Enter this in cell D12 and see what happens. If you enter it correctly, the result will be 6.

The sequence in which the 1-2-3 program performs computations is as follows:

First: Exponentiation
Second: Multiplication and Division
Third: Addition and Subtraction

Just like high school algebra! Within each level of precedence, the calculations are performed from left to right. In the example above, the first operation performed is 6 divided by 2. Next, starting from the left, 4 is added to 3, and then 1 is subtracted for a result of 6.

If you wish to perform the computations in some other sequence, what can you do? Rearranging the formula is not always the answer. You can control the sequence of computations in 1-2-3 by using parentheses. The 1-2-3 program will always perform calculations inside a set of parentheses before doing any other arithmetic operations. Suppose in the example above that you want to add 4 and 6 before dividing by 2. Using parentheses, the formula would look as follows: **(4+6)/2-1**. Try it and see if you get 4 as the answer.

It is also possible to have several sets of parentheses in a single formula. For example: **9+(9*2)/(7-4)**. 1-2-3 will perform the operations inside both pairs of parentheses first (left set first), then do the division, and lastly do the addition. Enter this formula now. Your answer should be 15.

Parentheses may also be "nested" as shown in this example: **(9+(9*2))/3**. 1-2-3 will perform the operations in the innermost set of parentheses first and then will work outward to the next set. In this example, the program will multiply 9 by 2, add 9 to the result, and then divide by 3. The answer will be 9.

Without the parentheses, the result would be quite different. Working in the natural order of precedence, 1-2-3 would multiply 9 by 2, divide the result by 3, and add 9 for an answer of 15.

Parentheses are used fairly frequently in 1-2-3 programming to direct the computer to the proper sequence of computations. The one thing you must remember is that there must always be an equal number of left and right parentheses in a formula. The formula (123/7*(-1.2*81) is incorrect because there are two left parentheses and only one right parenthesis.

Formulas

Move the cursor to cell C15, type **10**, and press ENTER. Enter **5** in cell C16 and **4** in cell C17. Then move the cursor to cell A10 and type the following: **+C15+C16+C17**. Press ENTER, and 19 appears in cell A10. You have just typed a formula.

This particular formula computes the sum of cells C15, C16, and C17. The formula tells the program to take the value in cell C15 and add it to the values found in cells C16 and C17. You have to use a mathematical symbol like a Plus Sign (+) in front of the C15 to indicate to the 1-2-3 program that C15 is to be treated as a value and not as a label. The program performs the calculation, and the result appears in cell A10. At the top of the next page are some other examples of formulas for you to try in cell A10.

Operator Key	Description	Example	Explanation	Answer
+ Plus Sign	Addition	123+456	Adds 123 and 456	579
- Dash	Subtraction	123-81	Subtracts 81 from 123	42
* Asterisk	Multiplication	123*1.2	Multiplies 123 by 1.2	147.6
/ Slash	Division	123/7	Divides 123 by 7	17.571
^ Caret	Exponentiation	123^2	Squares 123	15129

Example	Explanation	Answer
+C15+C16+C17	Adds the values in C16 and C17 to the value in C15	19
+C15-C16+C17	Subtracts the value in C16 from the value in C15 and then adds the value in C17	9
5*C16	Multiplies the value in C16 by 5	25
+C15/C16	Divides the value in C15 by the value in C16	2
+C17*(C16-1)	Subtracts 1 from the value in C16 and multiplies the result by the value in C17	16
(C15-2)/C17	Subtracts 2 from the value in C15 and divides the result by the value in C17	2
-C16^3	Makes the value in C16 negative and then raises it to the 3rd power	-125

This formula method of computation is one of the most important features of the 1-2-3 program. It is what makes spreadsheet programs so flexible and powerful. The spreadsheet models on your Template Disk use many formulas.

SPECIAL FUNCTION COMMANDS

The first formula shown in the table at the bottom of the previous page is +C15+C16+C17. 1-2-3 has a special summation function that allows you to add a row or a column of figures quickly. To demonstrate this function, move the cursor to cell A11, type @SUM(C15.C17), and press ENTER. The AT (@) key is above the number 2 key on the standard IBM PC keyboard.

Entering @SUM tells 1-2-3 to use the summation function. The first cell, C15, tells the computer where to begin the addition, and the last cell, C17, tells the computer the last cell to include in the total. This method is particularly useful for summing long rows or columns. You should note that when you enter the Period (.) key, the computer responds with two periods (..). This is perfectly normal.

The 1-2-3 program contains many special function commands besides @SUM. A partial list includes @SQRT for square root, @AVG to compute the average value, @MAX to find the maximum value in a range, and @NPV for net present value. These and other special function commands are discussed in detail in Appendix C of this manual.

FORMULA POINTING

The 1-2-3 program provides an alternate way to enter formulas and special function commands. The pointing technique can be used any time you use a cell reference in a formula or in a special function command. It can be used with all arithmetic operations. Instead of typing the cell references, pointing allows you to use the arrow keys to point to the cells you want to enter. Some people make extensive use of pointing; others use it only occasionally.

To demonstrate pointing, follow the steps below to enter the formula **+C15-C16** in cell A12:

1. Make sure you are in the READY mode.
2. Move the cursor to cell A12.
3. Press the Plus Sign (+).
4. Move the cursor to cell C15.
5. Press the Minus Sign (-).
6. Move the cursor to cell C16.
7. Press ENTER.

The formula +C15-C16 shows up in the control panel and the answer (5) appears in cell A12.

FILE COMMANDS (/F)

File Save

You are now going to electronically transfer the doodles on your screen from memory in the computer (where they currently reside) to a permanent storage area. This will allow you to recall the doodles to your screen any time you want without having to type them all in again.

The permanent storage area is the Template Disk provided with this workbook. The Template Disk should already be in drive B. (If your computer has a hard disk drive, see the footnote below.)[2] Now press the Slash key and then type F (for File). The subcommand Save is what you want. Press S now for Save. The program will respond with a message asking you to enter the name of the file. With Version 1A, you will see in the Control Panel some other strange names. These are the names of files already on your Template Disk.

Type the name **DOODLES** and press the ENTER key. (File names cannot be longer than eight letters or numbers; either capital or lowercase letters are acceptable; no punctuation or spaces allowed.) The disk drive will jump to life and then after a few seconds will stop. You have now saved your doodles as a file called DOODLES. On Version 2, 2.01, and 2.2, 1-2-3 will add .WK1 to the end of your file name.

If there were already a file named DOODLES on the disk, the program would ask you to make the following decision:

Cancel   Replace   Backup (Version 2.2 only)

You cannot have two files with the same name on the storage disk. If you press **R**, the old file will be replaced with the new one. If you don't want to replace the old file, you would press **C**. You would then go through the File Save command sequence again and choose another name for the new file.

With the Template Disk still in the drive, let's erase the worksheet from the screen. Press the Slash key and then type W (for Worksheet). Press E (for Erase) and Y (for Yes). Don't worry, this command will not erase the file from the disk. The file is erased only from the screen.

File Retrieve

After using the Worksheet Erase command, you should be looking at a blank worksheet. Let's bring the doodles back on the screen now. Enter /F to get the File subcommands again and then press R to select the Retrieve subcommand. The 1-2-3 program responds as follows:

Enter name of file to retrieve:

You can type the name **DOODLES** and press ENTER, or you may use the Right Arrow key to move the cursor over and highlight the file name DOODLES in the Control Panel, and then press ENTER. Let's use the second approach. With Lotus 1-2-3 Version 2, 2.01, and 2.2, the files are listed al-

phabetically. Press the Right Arrow key repeatedly until the cursor is highlighting the file name DOODLES. Then press ENTER. The disk drive will start up and the doodles will soon appear on the screen. The cursor will appear in exactly the same spot it was left when the file was saved.

With Version 2.2 there is a third approach possible for retrieving a file. After typing /FR, press the F3 (Name) key. This provides a full screen menu of all files on the Template Disk. Use the Arrow keys to highlight the appropriate file name and press ENTER.

Although the file DOODLES is now on the screen, it is also still recorded on the disk. It has simply been "read" into the computer. It will stay on the disk and can be used over and over until you formally erase it.

File Erase

To erase a file from the disk, enter /FEW (File Erase Worksheet) and then type or point to the name of the file to be erased. Press ENTER and then **Y** for Yes. Use this command to erase the DOODLES file from the disk now.

Please note the difference between the three erase commands. Range Erase is used to erase specified cells on a worksheet. Worksheet Erase is used to erase the entire worksheet from the screen. File Erase is used to erase a file from the disk.

NAME FILE

A special file on the Template Disk is called the NAME file. Retrieve this file now by typing /FR, then type (or point to) the file NAME, and press ENTER. As mentioned above, with Version 2.2, the file can be selected by pressing the F3 key and using the Arrow keys. This file asks you for your name and is used later when printing the preprogrammed problem solutions. You run NAME only once, so make sure you follow the in-

---

[2] The preprogrammed problems in this workbook require that the Template Disk be used in drive A or drive B. Furthermore, the Lotus 1-2-3 program must be configured to look for this disk in the appropriate drive (referred to as the default drive). Before continuing with this lesson, type /WGDD. If the directory is set at A:\ or B:\, this is okay. Just press ENTER and then Q to Quit. If the current directory is set at anything else, press the ESC key and enter A:\ or B:\ whichever is appropriate. Then press ENTER and Q to Quit.

structions carefully. After the file NAME has been loaded, press ENTER and you will see a screen requesting that you enter your name. Please type your name and then press ENTER twice. Failure to follow this step properly will destroy a file on your disk, and you will not be able to turn in the printouts required by your instructor.

WHAT-IF ANALYSIS

As mentioned previously, the use of formulas in spreadsheet models is a very important feature of the 1-2-3 program. It adds power and flexibility to the models and allows what-if analysis to be performed easily.

To demonstrate this form of analysis, a file on your Template Disk called LESSON1 will be used. Follow the steps below:

1. With the statement that **Your name has now been saved on this disk** still on the screen, make sure you are in the READY mode (use ESC key if necessary).
2. Type **/FR** and then type (or point to) the file name **LESSON1**. Press ENTER. The file LESSON1, which is a projected income statement for Easy Over Inc. for six months, should appear as shown in Illustration 2.
3. Formulas are used in most cells of this model to compute the values that appear. The formulas

that are used in this model are summarized as follows:

Sales: each month's sales increase 2% over the previous month
Selling expenses: 60% of each month's sales
General expenses: $19 each month
Total expenses: sum of selling and general expenses
Net income: sales less total expenses

Move the cursor to cell D7. Look at the Control Panel at the top of the screen to see the formula stored in that cell, +C7*1.02. This formula multiplies the value in cell C7, January sales, by 1.02. The formula indicates that February sales are expected to increase 2% over January sales. Move the cursor around the worksheet and examine the other formulas.

4. Let's perform what-if analysis with this income statement. Notice that May's net income is $24.30. What would happen to May's net income if January's sales were $110 instead of $100? To find out, move the cursor to cell C7, type the number **110** (just type it right over the 100), and press ENTER. What happens? The income statement is automatically updated as the input changes. Try **120**. Try **200**. This is referred to as what-if analysis. Now you are beginning to witness what an electronic spreadsheet is all about!

Illustration 2
Income Statement Saved
as File LESSON1

```
A1:                                                              READY

          A       B       C        D        E        F        G        H
 1
 2                             Easy Over Inc.
 3                           Net Income Projection
 4
 5                         Jan      Feb      Mar      Apr      May      Jun
 6                       -------  -------  -------  -------  -------  -------
 7  Sales               $100.00  $102.00  $104.04  $106.12  $108.24  $110.41
 8
 9  Selling expenses     $60.00   $61.20   $62.42   $63.67   $64.95   $66.24
10  General expenses      19.00    19.00    19.00    19.00    19.00    19.00
11                       -------  -------  -------  -------  -------  -------
12  Total expenses        $79.00   $80.20   $81.42   $82.67   $83.95   $85.24
13                       -------  -------  -------  -------  -------  -------
14  Net income           $21.00   $21.80   $22.62   $23.45   $24.30   $25.16
15                       =======  =======  =======  =======  =======  =======
16
17
18
19
20
```

NUMERICAL INPUT ERRORS

Certain entries in cell C7 will cause strange results. For example, enter the number **150** in cell C7. Notice that May's net income appears to be off by a penny. This is because 1-2-3 rounds off each cell to the nearest penny for screen presentation, but it internally stores the value of each cell up to fifteen decimal places. Internally, it is computing net income correctly, but when it rounds off each cell to present the result, occasionally a rounding difference will occur. There is a special function command (@ROUND) discussed in Appendix C that will correct this problem.

Enter **1,000** in cell C7 and press ENTER. From the result, you can see that numbers are not to be entered with commas! Press ESC to get back to the READY mode.

Now type **1000** (one thousand) and press ENTER. What happens? The number doesn't show up in the cell, does it? It is too large for the cell, and the result you see is the way 1-2-3 tells you this.

Now type the word **HELLO** in cell C7 and press ENTER. Under Version 1A and Versions 2.01 and 2.2, the reason that zeros appear in many cells is that the 1-2-3 program assigns the numerical value of zero to all labels. Since cell C7 is now a label, it is given the value of zero and this subsequently affects many other cells. Under Version 2, labels are not given a numerical value. Therefore, any cell with a value dependent on C7 will show ERR.

Now reset the value in cell C7 to **100**. The examples above demonstrate typical input errors. Keep them in mind when entering numerical data.

PRINT COMMANDS (/P)

Normal Printing

You will now use the Print command to print the six-month income projections on a printer. If you do not have a printer hooked up to your computer, skip this for now. You can always come back to it later.

The **Print** command requires that the hardware configuration is properly installed on your Lotus 1-2-3 System disk. Please see your instructor if you have problems getting your worksheet to print. The basic steps to print the worksheet LESSON1 are as follows:

1. Turn the printer on and make sure it is "On Line."

2. Load the file to be printed if it is not on your screen (**/FR LESSON1**).

3. Press the Slash key and then type **P** to select the Print command.

4. In response to Printer or File, press **P** to indicate Printer. (On Version 2.2, the Print Settings sheet appears on the screen. The Print Settings sheet display can be turned off and on by pressing the F6 (Window) key.)

5. Press **R** to indicate your selection of Range.

6. Now type the range to be printed and press ENTER. In this case, type **A1.H15** to indicate the corners and press ENTER.

7. If necessary, press **L** (Line) several times to position the paper in the printer so that the printing begins at the top of a page.

8. Press **A** (Align). This command tells the printer that you are at the top of a new page.

9. Press **G** (Go) to begin printing. The printer should now spring to life and print out the worksheet exactly as you see it on the screen.

10. Press **P** (Page) to eject the page just printed from the printer.

11. When you are done with the Print command, press **Q** to Quit.

Even though you have now left the print command, the range that you entered in Step 6 above will be remembered by the computer and will not need to be entered again when reprinting LESSON1.

If you cannot get your printer to work, refer to the Lotus 1-2-3 manual or contact your instructor for more detailed assistance. Also, see Appendix B (Resolving Problems) in this manual for some additional suggestions.

Should you want to halt the printing before it finishes the range you have specified, press the CTRL and BREAK keys simultaneously to stop the printing. The Mode Indicator will change from WAIT to READY, but some printers will print a few more lines before stopping.

Unformatted Printing

There are many print options available to alter borders, margins, page length, etc. These options are accessed by selecting Options from the print menu. One very popular option is to maximize print space on a page by eliminating all margins, borders, and page breaks. To print an unformatted worksheet, enter the basic print commands shown above but before typing G (Step 9), type **OOUQ** (Options Other Unformatted Quit). Use this option whenever you want to get rid of gaps or skips in your printout.

Compressed Mode

Many printers will print up to 80 characters per line, about the same as a typewriter. Lotus 1-2-3 is designed to print 72 characters per line which is the width of the worksheet seen on the monitor. If you are printing a worksheet that is wider than 72 characters, the additional columns will be printed automatically on later pages.

An alternative is to print wide spreadsheets in compressed mode. Check with your instructor to determine if your printer is able to compress print. If it can, follow these instructions to print LESSON1 in compressed mode.

1. Press the Slash key and then type **P** to select the Print command.
2. In response to Printer or File, press **P** to indicate Printer.
3. Press **R** to indicate your selection of Range. Note that the computer remembers your range (A1.H15). Simply press ENTER to accept the range offered.
4. Type **OOU** (Options Other Unformatted) to get unformatted printing (eliminate the page breaks, etc.).
5. Type **MR** (Margins Right). Ordinarily, you would enter a number equal to or higher than the width of the worksheet you are printing. If you are printing a worksheet that is 12 columns wide and each column contains 9 characters (the standard width), you would set the right margin to at least **108** (12 X 9 = 108). With LESSON1, you will not need to reset the right margin because the template is not more than 72 characters wide. Simply press ENTER.
6. Type **S** (Setup) and enter the correct printer setup code. For IBM and Epson printers, the setup code for compressed printing is **\015** (note that this sequence uses the Backslash (\) key instead of the Slash (/) key. Press ENTER and then press **Q** (Quit).
7. Press **A** (Align).
8. Press **G** (Go) to begin printing.
9. Press **P** (Page) to eject the page just printed from the printer.
10. Return the printer to regular (non-compressed) print. To do this, type **OS** (Options Setup), press ESC to clear the setup string, type **\018** (IBM and Epson printers), and press ENTER.

Then type **MR** (Margins Right), enter **76**, press ENTER, and then press **Q** (Quit).
11. Press **Q** to Quit. This should get you back to the READY mode.

Print Screen (the PRTSC key)

The PRINT SCREEN (PRTSC) key on the IBM PC can be used in a limited fashion to print spreadsheet models. On older keyboards, when the PRTSC key and the SHIFT key are pressed at the same time, the printer will print all data shown on the screen. On newer keyboards, only the PRINT SCREEN key on the upper right side of the keyboard needs to be pressed. Try it now with LESSON1 on your screen. You will note that the worksheet borders also print.

Printing Cell Contents

It is possible to print your model in a cell-by-cell fashion disclosing all of the formulas. Thus, you can have a "hard copy" record of your formulas for future reference. To print a list of the cell contents of LESSON1, for example, use the following steps:

1. Press **/P** to select the Print command.
2. Press **P** to select the Printer option.
3. Press **R** to select the Range option.
4. Type the range A1.H15 and then press ENTER (or just press ENTER to accept the range that is offered).
5. Press **O** to select Options.
6. Press **O** again to select Other.
7. Press **C** for Cell-Formulas.
8. Press **Q** to Quit.
9. Type **OOUQ** (Options Other Unformatted Quit) to get unformatted printing (eliminate the page breaks, etc.).
10. Press **A** to Align.
11. Press **G** to begin printing.
12. When the printing is done, type **OOAQ** (Options Other As-Displayed Quit) to return to normal (As-Displayed) print.
13. Press **P** to eject the Page.
14. Press **Q** to Quit.

GRAPHS

Lotus 1-2-3 has the capability to display spreadsheet figures graphically on your screen and to print them on a printer. Graphs can be constructed and then saved just like spreadsheets. However, not all personal computers have the capability of displaying or printing graphics. Consult your instructor on the capabilities of your personal computer. Skip this section for now if you cannot display graphics on you screen. You can always come back to it later.

If you have a graphics configuration, press the F10 key now. What you should see is a previously constructed bar graph based on LESSON1 plotting monthly sales and total expenses. This is shown in Illustration 3 below. A bar graph is one of several graph options (line graphs, bar graphs, pie graphs, etc.). The commands to construct a graph are fairly extensive and are covered in Lesson 3 of this manual. When you are done examining the bar graph, press any key to return to the spreadsheet.

Using the F10 key, you can perform what-if graphing. Each time you enter new values in a data range, pressing F10 will let you graphically see the impact immediately. Try this out by entering new values in cell C7 and then pressing F10.

The print commands will not print out a graph. Graphs can be printed using the PrintGraph program. This is also discussed in Lesson 3.

OTHER FEATURES OF THE LOTUS 1-2-3 PROGRAM

The Lotus 1-2-3 program contains many options and features not previously discussed. The following is a list of some of the more common features that are found on the spreadsheet files that accompany your workbook.

1. Protected cells. It is possible to lock cells so that no entry can be made into them. This is a very helpful feature to prevent someone from erasing or mistakenly entering information in an incorrect cell.
2. Column width. The standard column width is nine characters. This can be changed to other widths.
3. Value formats. It is possible to program 1-2-3 to show values with commas, dollar signs, percent signs, as integers, etc.
4. Column or row freeze. You can program 1-2-3 to always leave certain columns or rows on the screen no matter where the cursor is.

Illustration 3
Bar Graph Plotting Sales and
Total Expenses

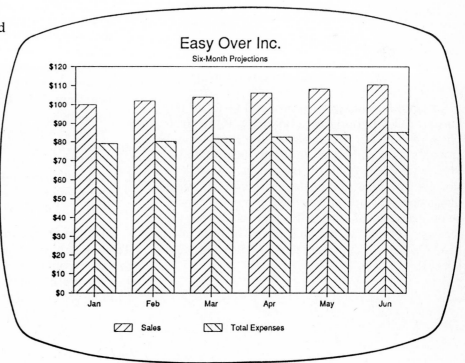

5. Split screen (windows). You may split the screen into two sections and simultaneously view separate portions of a worksheet.

6. Manual recalculation. All calculations in DOODLES and LESSON1 were performed instantly by the program. It is possible to turn the automatic recalculation feature "off." After this is done, recalculations will only occur when the F9 key is pressed.

7. Macros. When working the problems in this workbook, you will occasionally be instructed to hold down the ALT key and press another key. When you follow these instructions, you are using a macro. A macro is a keyboard command which can be used to simplify commands for users. For example, the Print command demonstrated above took several keystrokes to execute. The developer of a spreadsheet model can preprogram it with a macro so that when the user presses the ALT key and a letter key, the entire Print command is automatically executed. Macros are commonly used to print files, move and enter data, combine files, move the cursor to a specified location, set up a personalized menu system, and so forth. Virtually every keystroke and command you can type on the keyboard can be embedded in a macro. (See Lesson 4 for details.)

EXITING FROM LOTUS 1-2-3

To complete Lesson 1, you need to leave the Lotus 1-2-3 program now. Type /QY (Quit Yes). With Version 2.2, if you have not already saved your file, you will be asked if you wish to do so. Then type E (Exit) to leave the program. With Version 1A, you need to type one more Y (Yes). When this is done, the operating system prompt (A>) will be on the screen. If, during this process, you see the messages "Non System Disk..." or "Insert COMMAND.COM disk...," insert the DOS disk and press ENTER.

FORMATTING AND PREPARING A DISK

As mentioned previously, you may need another disk for storing your answer templates because the Template Disk will not hold many extra files. You will fill up the Template Disk rather quickly once you begin the preprogrammed problems, thus it is important that you prepare the extra storage disk now. Even if you are familiar with the formatting procedure, follow the instructions below to format the disk and copy a file from your Template Disk to your newly formatted disk.

The procedure used to prepare a diskette to store files is called formatting a disk. In addition, a file called INIT.PRN must be copied onto all new template disks. This file is needed to print out the files on the Template Disk. If you have a computer system with two floppy disk drives, use the instructions below to prepare your blank diskette to store Lotus 1-2-3 files. If your computer system has a hard disk, follow your instructor's directions for formatting.

1. Insert the DOS disk in drive A, if it is not already there.
2. At the A> prompt, type **FORMAT B:** (be sure to type the colon) and press ENTER.
3. Insert a blank diskette in drive B and press ENTER. (Caution: Formatting erases anything that is stored on the diskette. If you are reusing a diskette, make sure there are no files that you may need in the future.)
4. When the formatting is done, press N in response to "Format Another?"
5. Remove the DOS disk from drive A and insert the Template Disk that came with this workbook.
6. At the A> prompt, type **COPY INIT.PRN B:** (again, be sure to type the colon) and press ENTER.
7. When the copying is done, remove both disks and turn off the computer. Label the new disk as "1-2-3 File Disk."

After completing the formatting and copying instructions above, you are finished with Lesson 1. You are encouraged at this point to read Appendix B of the workbook. It provides a good review of common errors made by beginners.

LESSON 2
BASIC SPREADSHEET MODELING

Learning Objectives

Topics introduced in this lesson are:
- designing a simple income statement model
- expanding the model from one month to six months using the Copy command
- formatting values (Worksheet Format and Range Format commands)
- aligning labels (cell alignment and Range Label-alignment commands)
- entering underlines, rules, and borders
- using the following additional commands:
  - Worksheet Global Column-width
  - Worksheet Global Recalculation
  - Worksheet Global Protection
  - Worksheet Global Zero
  - Worksheet Insert
  - Worksheet Delete
  - Worksheet Column-width
  - Worksheet Titles
  - Worksheet Window
  - Worksheet Status
  - Range Name
  - Range Justify
  - Range Protect and Range Unprotect
  - Move
  - System

WORKSHEET SETUP AND FORMULAS

Before you begin this lesson, the 1-2-3 program should be loaded, your Template Disk should be in drive B, and you should be staring at a blank worksheet. Refer to Lesson 1 if you need help loading the program.

Let's set up a simple income statement. Enter the labels listed at the top of the next column. The cells where you are to put the labels are shown on the left, followed by a colon. The labels are shown on the right side of the colon. For example, A3:**Sales** means put the label **Sales** in cell A3 and then press ENTER (or an arrow key). Remember to use the

BACKSPACE key or the ESC key to correct errors. Note that several of these entries extend into column B.

> A3:**Sales**
> A5:**Selling expenses**
> A6:**General expenses**
> A8:**Total expenses**
> A10:**Net income**

Now let's enter some values into the statement. Enter the following amount for sales:

> C3:**100**

Next, assume that selling expenses are 60% of sales. You will enter a formula to compute selling expenses in cell C5. The formula will tell the program to take the value in cell C3, multiply it by .6, and put the result in cell C5. You have to use the Plus Sign (+) in front of the "C3" to indicate to the 1-2-3 program that C3 is to be treated as a value and not as a label. Enter the following formula for selling expenses:

> C5:**+C3*.6**

The 1-2-3 program will perform the calculation, and the result (60) will be entered in cell C5.

Now enter the value for general expenses in cell C6 as follows:

> C6:**19**

In cell C8, enter the sum of the two expenses.

> C8:**+C5+C6**

Now let's enter the last formula. Net income is computed by subtracting total expenses (C8) from sales (C3). Hence, the formula will be as follows:

> C10:**+C3-C8**

After you have entered the above formula, you will have completed the simple income statement. It should appear as shown in Illustration 4 at the top of the next page.

Illustration 4
Income Statement

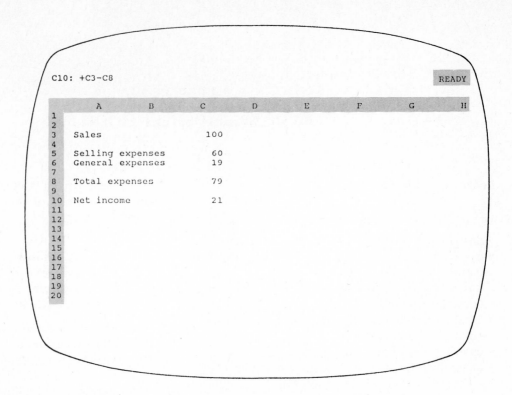

```
C10: +C3-C8                                                              READY

        A          B          C          D          E          F          G          H
 1
 2
 3   Sales                   100
 4
 5   Selling expenses         60
 6   General expenses         19
 7
 8   Total expenses           79
 9
10   Net income               21
11
12
13
14
15
16
17
18
19
20
```

LABEL ALIGNMENT

To begin exploring spreadsheet commands in detail, let's expand the income statement developed above from one month to six months. Move the cursor to cell C1, enter the letters JAN (short for January), and press ENTER. Type in headings for each month by entering the following:

> D1:FEB
> E1:MAR
> F1:APR
> G1:MAY
> H1:JUN
> I1:TOTAL

Notice that the labels appear in the cells indicated, but they are not aligned above the numbers. This is because values are aligned to the right side of cells, and labels are aligned to the left. Label alignment can be changed in one of three ways: a single cell can be realigned; a specific range of labels can be realigned; or all labels on the worksheet can be realigned. The procedures for the first two options will be discussed below. The third option (all labels on the worksheet) is rarely used and will not be discussed.

Aligning a Label in a Single Cell

The label in a single cell can be realigned by putting a code character in front of the label. Type each of the following examples in cell C1 and watch what happens (press ENTER after each example):

Code Character	Example	Result
Quotation mark	"JAN	Right aligned
Apostrophe	'JAN	Left aligned
Caret	^JAN	Centered
Backslash	\JAN	Repeating

Aligning Labels in a Range

Using the Range command, you can affect the alignment of labels on a portion of the worksheet. The labels in a range can be right aligned, left aligned, or centered. To realign the labels in row 1 using the Range command, position the cursor in cell C1 and enter /RLC (Range Label Center).

Let's use the pointing technique to indicate the range. Press the Right Arrow key six times to expand the range to C1..I1 and press ENTER. The labels in the range are now centered in their cells.

COPY (/C)

The **Copy** command allows you to take the contents of one cell and copy it into another cell. It also allows you to copy the contents of a range of cells (source range) into another range of cells (target range). This is an extremely important and powerful command.

To demonstrate the Copy command, let's fill in the numbers for each month on your income statement. Assume that sales will increase by 2% per month. In other words, you want February's sales to be 2% greater than January's, March's sales to be 2% greater than February's, and so forth. To compute February's sales, you want to tell the computer to multiply January's sales, cell C3, by 1.02. The result will be entered in cell D3. Enter the following formula in cell D3:

$$D3:+C3*1.02$$

Since you want this 2% increase to be computed for each month, you can now use the Copy command to enter the correct formula in each of the remaining sales cells. With the cursor in cell D3, press the Slash (/) key and then select the **Copy**

command. In the Control Panel, you will see the following:

Enter range to copy FROM: D3..D3

The program is asking you to identify the source range. In this case, your source range is simply one cell, since you are only interested in copying the formula in cell D3. The computer already shows this cell (D3..D3) as the source range, so simply press ENTER now. If there were a range of cells to be copied, you would enter that range (by pointing or typing) before pressing ENTER. This will be demonstrated later.

Now that the source range has been entered, the program wants to know what the target range is. In other words, it wants to know TO which cells the contents of cell D3 are to be copied. Since the remaining sales figures are to appear in cells E3 through H3, enter **E3**, press the Period (.) key, and enter **H3**. Press ENTER and watch what happens. Bingo! The formulas and the answers are put into cells E3 through H3 as shown in Illustration 5. The numbers are inconsistent in format, some having no decimal point and others having a decimal point followed by several digits, but you will take care of this problem later.

Illustration 5
Income Statement After
Copying of Sales Cells

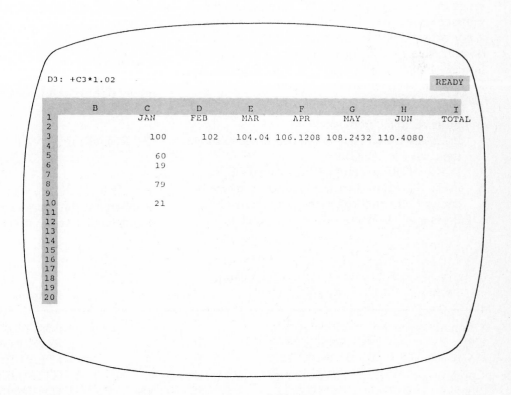

Notice the sequence of sales figures. Each month is a 2% increase over the previous month. The formula in cell D3 is +C3*1.02. Move the cursor to cell E3 and check the formula in that cell. You will see that the formula is +D3*1.02. Move the cursor to F3, G3, and H3 and look at the formulas. You will find that the formula in cell D3 was not copied exactly, but rather was modified as it moved from cell to cell.

The Copy command copies the formula from cell to cell and automatically modifies the formula to follow the same pattern as in the original formula. In this case, the original formula in cell D3 uses a value from the cell to its immediate left (C3). Thus, when copying this formula, each new formula will also use a value from the cell to its immediate left. When copying formulas, the 1-2-3 program assumes that all cell references are "relative" and are to be modified from cell to cell.

What if you want to copy a formula but you do not want the cell references to change? There is a simple way to do this. By entering a Dollar Sign ($) in front of any cell reference used in a formula, you tell the computer that the cell reference is "absolute" (does not change). To compare the effects of absolute versus relative copying of formulas, examine the table shown at the bottom of the page.

The above example of copying involved a source range that was a single cell (D3). As mentioned previously, you can also use the Copy command to copy several formulas (a range) at once. To demonstrate this, let's copy each of the remaining January formulas and values to the other months. Perform the following steps:

1. Position the cursor in cell C5.
2. Enter /C to begin the copying.
3. Press the Down Arrow key five times to move the cursor to cell C10.
4. Press ENTER to complete the source range.
5. Press the Right Arrow key once to move the cursor to the first cell in the target range (D5).
6. Press the Period key to lock in your choice.

7. Press the Right Arrow key four times to move the cursor to the ending point in the target range (H5). Note that when the source range is more than one cell, the target range indicates only where the first cell in the source range is to be placed. Hence, the target range is only a single row of cells and not a block of cells.
8. Press ENTER to complete the copying.

In a few short steps, you have entered income statement data for six months! It is now time to fill in the TOTAL column. Move the cursor to cell I3 and enter the following formula to compute total sales for the six-month period:

I3:@SUM(C3.H3)

(For a review of the @SUM function see Lesson 1 or Appendix C.) Now you will copy this summation formula to rows 5 through 10 using the following steps:

1. Position the cursor in cell I3.
2. Enter /C to begin the copying.
3. Press ENTER to complete the source range.
4. Enter I5.I10 and press ENTER for the target range.
5. Move the cursor to cell I7, press /RE, then press the ENTER key. This step is necessary because the summation formula has been copied into cell I7 but is not needed there. Repeat this in cell I9.

After copying, your income statement should appear as shown in Illustration 6 at the top of the next page. The income statement looks a little messy right now, but basically it is done!

FORMATTING VALUES ON THE ENTIRE WORKSHEET

Now it is time to clean up the appearance of the numbers on the worksheet. This is called formatting values. To format values on the entire work-

| | C3 is Absolute | | C3 is Relative | |
	Formula	Value	Formula	Value
Original Formula	D3:$C$3*1.02	102.00	D3:C3*1.02	102.00
Copy	E3:$C$3*1.02	102.00	E3:D3*1.02	104.04
Copy	F3:$C$3*1.02	102.00	F3:E3*1.02	106.12
Copy	G3:$C$3*1.02	102.00	G3:F3*1.02	108.24
Copy	H3:$C$3*1.02	102.00	H3:G3*1.02	110.41

Illustration 6
Completed Income
Statement (Columns B
Through I)

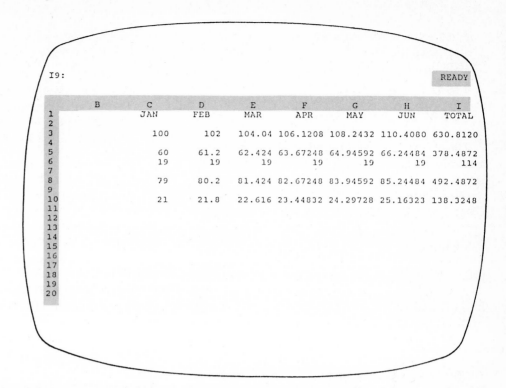

	B	C	D	E	F	G	H	I
		JAN	FEB	MAR	APR	MAY	JUN	TOTAL
1								
2								
3		100	102	104.04	106.1208	108.2432	110.4080	630.8120
4								
5		60	61.2	62.424	63.67248	64.94592	66.24484	378.4872
6		19	19	19	19	19	19	114
7								
8		79	80.2	81.424	82.67248	83.94592	85.24484	492.4872
9								
10		21	21.8	22.616	23.44832	24.29728	25.16323	138.3248
11								
12								
13								
14								
15								
16								
17								
18								
19								
20								

I9:   READY

sheet, enter /WGF now. (On Version 2.2, a Global Settings sheet appears on the screen. This setting sheet display can be turned off and on by pressing the F6 key.) The Control Panel will display the menu of options available to you which are listed below. Versions 2, 2.01, and 2.2 also include the command Hidden.

>   Fixed
>   Scientific
>   Currency
>   ,
>   General
>   +/-
>   Percent
>   Date
>   Text

Press **F** to examine the Fixed option. You are asked the number of decimal places to be shown.

The computer offers the choice of two decimal places. You may either accept two decimal places by pressing ENTER, or you may type the desired number of places and then press ENTER. Let's accept the computer's offer of two decimal places. Simply press ENTER and watch what happens! Instantly, all values are displayed with two decimal places.

Now let's try the same thing with zero decimal places. Enter **/WGFF** to select the Fixed option. Now type in **0** (zero) and press ENTER. The screen now shows all integers.

Take a minute now and try the other formats listed below. These are the formats most frequently used in 1-2-3. Enter **/WGF** and then either use the arrow keys to move the menu pointer to the format of your choice, or enter the first letter of your choice. The table below lists each format and its result.

Format	Result
Fixed	Fixed number of decimals places (0-15). No commas used.
Currency	Numbers expressed as dollars and cents. Dollar signs before each entry. Commas between thousands. Negative numbers in parentheses.
,(comma)	Same as the Currency format without the dollar signs.
General	Initial display format shown.
Percent	All numbers expressed as percents.
Text	Shows the formulas in each cell.
Hidden	Hides all entries on the worksheet (Version 2 and Version 2.01 only)

After you have experimented with these formats, please reset the worksheet to the General format (/WGFG).

FORMATTING A RANGE OF VALUES

The above commands apply to the worksheet as a whole. Values can also be formatted using the Range command, which affects a smaller grouping of cells. To demonstrate this, move the cursor to cell C3 and type /RF. You will now see the same list of options that were available under the Worksheet command. Let's put all worksheet figures in the Currency format. Press C (for Currency) and then press ENTER to accept the computer's offer of two decimal places. Type the range C3.I10 and press ENTER again.

Next, use the following steps to format row 6 using the , (comma) format and the pointing technique:

1. Move the cursor to cell C6.
2. Enter /RF, (be sure you type the comma!).
3. Press ENTER to accept two decimal places.
4. Press the Right Arrow key six times to move the cursor to column I.
5. Press ENTER.

UNDERLINES AND BORDERS

To improve appearance and readability, let's now add underlines, double underlines, and borders in appropriate locations in our model. Move the cursor to cell C2 where we will begin underlining the month headings. Underlines for headings should be at least as long as the headings themselves and should have at least one blank space between the columns. Each cell generally holds nine characters, and these are no exception. Let's go with underlines that are seven characters long and are centered in each cell. In cell C2, press the Space Bar, then type seven dashes (Minus Signs), and press ENTER.

Now copy this to the other cells in row 2:

1. Enter /C and press ENTER.
2. Press the Right Arrow key once.
3. Press the Period key.
4. Press the Right Arrow key five more times.
5. Press ENTER.

The underlines also need to be placed in row 7. Use the following steps to copy the row of dashes in row 2 to row 7:

1. With the cursor in cell C2, press /C.
2. To indicate the source range, type C2.I2 and press ENTER.
3. Move the cursor to cell C7 and press ENTER.

Use the same three steps above to copy the underlines to row 9. (In Step 3, move the cursor to cell C9, rather than cell C7.)

In cell C11, we will put a double underline. Move the cursor to cell C11 and press the Space Bar, then type seven Equal Signs (=), and press ENTER. Use the Copy command to copy the Equal Signs to cells D11 through I11. If you need assistance, refer to the five steps above.

As you may recall, the Backslash (\) key is the code character for repeating labels. Let's add a border to the bottom of the income statement by using the Backslash key. Move the cursor to cell A13. Press the Backslash key, then press the Asterisk (*) key, and press ENTER. Cell A13 should now be filled with asterisks.

With the cursor in cell A13, type /C and press ENTER to complete the source range. Then type B13.I13 to complete the target range. Press ENTER. Your completed income statement should appear as shown in Illustration 7 at the top of the next page.

SAVE YOUR WORK

Before moving on to the next section, save your spreadsheet model on your Template Disk. Make sure you are in the READY mode and your Template Disk is in drive B. Type /FS LESSON2 and press ENTER.

Although you will now begin experimenting with some commands that alter the worksheet you have just saved, it should be noted that your manipulations will not affect the saved version of LESSON2 on the Template Disk. The alterations that you make to the income statement model change the worksheet only as it appears on the screen. In order to change the version of LESSON2 on the disk, you would have to use the File Save command again.

WORKSHEET COMMANDS

As discussed in Lesson 1, Worksheet commands are general commands that affect the entire spread-

Illustration 7
Completed Income
Statement with
Underlines and
Border (Columns A
Through H)

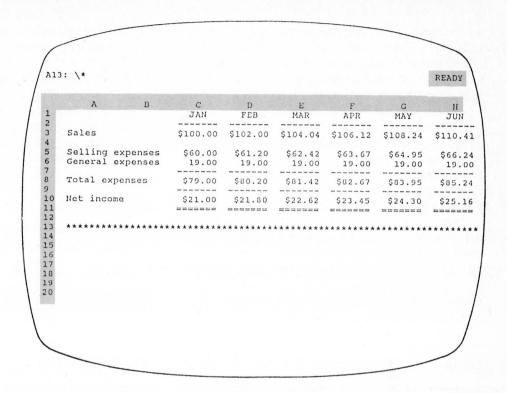

```
A13: \*                                                              READY

          A         B        C         D         E         F         G         H
 1                          JAN       FEB       MAR       APR       MAY       JUN
 2                        -------   -------   -------   -------   -------   -------
 3   Sales               $100.00   $102.00   $104.04   $106.12   $108.24   $110.41
 4
 5   Selling expenses     $60.00    $61.20    $62.42    $63.67    $64.95    $66.24
 6   General expenses      19.00     19.00     19.00     19.00     19.00     19.00
 7                        -------   -------   -------   -------   -------   -------
 8   Total expenses       $79.00    $80.20    $81.42    $82.67    $83.95    $85.24
 9                        -------   -------   -------   -------   -------   -------
10   Net income           $21.00    $21.80    $22.62    $23.45    $24.30    $25.16
11                        =======   =======   =======   =======   =======   =======
12
13   ****************************************************************************
14
15
16
17
18
19
20
```

sheet. The Worksheet Global Format (/WGF) and Worksheet Erase (/WE) commands have already been discussed. Several of the other Worksheet Global subcommands and the rest of the Worksheet commands (except Worksheet Page for Versions 2, 2.01, and 2.2, and the Learn command on Version 2.2) will now be discussed.

Global Column-Width (/WGC)

The standard column width (9 characters) may be changed to any number of characters between 1 and 240. You may want wide cells to be able to enter large numbers, or narrow cells to fit more columns on the screen. This command is global. It affects all columns. The column width for a single column can be adjusted using the Column-Width command (/WC). This will be discussed later.

To change the column width of all columns, enter /WGC now. You will be asked to enter a column width; enter 8 and press ENTER. Bingo! All the columns are shortened by one space. This allows both column A and column I to be seen on the screen at the same time.

Now try a column width of 15. Note that only four columns appear on the screen. Next, try a column width of 5. Here there is a surprise. You can probably guess what happened. The columns became too narrow to present the numbers and labels

fully. Now try a column width of 9. As you can see from the result, the column-width choice does not affect actual cell contents. It simply affects the screen presentation.

Global Recalculation (/WGR)

You can control the order in which 1-2-3 performs its calculations. The three options are Columnwise, Rowwise, or Natural. Columnwise means that the computer begins calculations in cell A1, moves down column A, then moves to cell B1, goes down that column, and so forth. Rowwise, as you might expect, begins calculations in cell A1 and then, moving left to right, moves down the worksheet row by row. 1-2-3 normally recalculates in the method called Natural. Under this method, 1-2-3 evaluates the worksheet to determine the most appropriate starting cell and sequence of cells for performing calculations. In your income statement the order of recalculation is not important, but in some worksheets it is.

The Recalculation options for Automatic, Manual, and Iteration relate to when recalculation occurs. Automatic is the way the program recalculates now. Any time a new number (input) is entered in cell C3, many of the other numbers are changed automatically. On larger worksheets with many inputs, you may wish to change several inputs before the recalculation occurs. You can change the recalculation from Automatic to Manual. In the Manual mode, you have to tell the computer when to recalculate the numbers.

To demonstrate this, type /WGRM. Next, enter the number **200** in cell C3 and press ENTER. What happens to the other numbers? Nothing, right? Now push the F9 key, and you will see the recalculation occur. You must press the F9 key each time you want a recalculation of your formulas when you are in the Manual mode.

The Iteration command will not be demonstrated here. The computer normally recalculates a worksheet only once after each input change. The Iteration option allows you to tell the computer to recalculate a worksheet several times with each change in input.

Type /WGRA now. That will get you back to the Automatic mode. Reset the value in cell C3 to **100**.

Global Protection (/WGP)

Your worksheet is currently unprotected, meaning that any cell's contents can be changed. You may, however, want to protect your worksheet or certain portions of it from accidental change. Since this 1-2-3 feature is mainly used to protect a specific range of cells, this command will be demonstrated later in conjunction with the Range Protect and Range Unprotect commands.

Global Zero (/WGZ)

Cells that have a value of zero are shown as blank cells if this command is used. This option is not available on Version 1A.

Insert (/WI)

This command is used to insert new columns or rows into a worksheet. Suppose you wish to insert the name of the company at the top of the income statement. Right now there is no place at the top of the worksheet to do this. Let's add another row to the worksheet.

Position the cursor in row 1 (the column doesn't matter), enter /WI, press **R** to indicate Row, and press ENTER to accept the computer's offer of the range. Instantly, the whole worksheet moves down a row so you can type the name of the company. Now position the cursor in cell D1 and type the name **Easy Over Inc.**

If you want to insert several rows, you can override the computer's range offer by typing (or point-ing to) your own range. For example, suppose you want to insert four more rows under the company name. To begin, move the cursor to row 2. Type /WIR and press the Down Arrow key three times. Finally, press ENTER. Instantly, four more rows are added to the statement.

The Insert command works for inserting rows and columns anywhere on the worksheet. It should also be noted that all formulas affected by an insertion are automatically changed by the program.

Delete (/WD)

This command deletes rows or columns from a worksheet. To demonstrate this, let's remove three of the four rows just inserted above. With the cursor in row 2, enter /WDR. Then, using the pointing technique, press the Down Arrow key two times. The highlighted area indicates the rows that will be deleted. Now press ENTER. The blank rows should disappear, and the whole worksheet should adjust upward by three rows. Again, all formulas affected by the deletion are automatically changed by the program.

Be careful with deletions because they are permanent. Once a row or column is deleted, the only way to recover it is to retype it. On Version 2.2 you can use the Undo command to recover a mistaken deletion.

Column-Width (/WC)

The Column command (Column-Width command in Version 1A) is used to change the width of a single column on the worksheet. This is more like a Range command than a Worksheet command. To demonstrate this command, move the cursor to cell C5 and type /WC. Press **S** to set the width of the current column (column C). Rather than accept the computer's offer of 9, type the number **15** and press ENTER. Notice that column C is now 15 characters wide.

Next, let's change the width of all the worksheet columns using the Global command. Type /WGC5 and press ENTER. As you can see, although the other columns are now 5 characters wide, column C remains 15 characters wide. The /WC command sets the column width for a specific column and it cannot be altered by changes in global column width.

To return column C to the global width (5), type /WC and this time press **R** (for Reset). Before moving on, enter /WGC9 and press ENTER to get back to the original format.

Titles (/WT)

The Titles command and the Window command (discussed below) are used to enhance the screen display of worksheets. The Titles command is used to "lock in" a row or column (or both) so that it always stays on the screen no matter where the cursor is. Move the cursor to cell A1. Notice that you cannot see the TOTAL column (column I) on the screen. You can pull column I onto the screen by moving the cursor to that column, but then you lose column A.

To demonstrate the use of the Titles command, move the cursor to cell C1 and enter /WT. The Titles command has four options: Both (horizontal and vertical), Horizontal, Vertical, and Clear (to eliminate the freeze on all rows and columns). Now press V and then move the cursor to column L. Notice what happens. Columns A and B are "frozen." The vertical option freezes all columns to the left of the cursor. The horizontal option freezes all rows above the cursor. As you can imagine, this command is very handy for viewing large worksheets. You are certainly welcome to experiment with these options.

Before you go to the next command, be sure to type /WTC to eliminate any fixed titles you have. Then move the cursor to cell A1.

Window (/WW)

The Window command allows you to split the screen into two sections and view separate portions of the worksheet simultaneously. It is a very useful command once it is mastered.

Let's use the Window command to view the edges of the income statement (e.g., column A and column I) simultaneously. Move the cursor to column D and enter /WW. You are now presented with five options: Horizontal, Vertical, Sync (both windows scroll together), Unsync, and Clear.

Press the letter V. What you see now is the screen split vertically. Press the F6 key several times and you will see the cursor jump from the left window to the right window and back again. Move the cursor to the right window. Then use the Right Arrow key to move the cursor to column I. You can now see both edges of the income statement at once!

The primary advantage of the Window command is that it allows you to enter some input in a cell at one edge of the worksheet and see the immediate effect in a cell at the other edge. For example, suppose you want to know what your January

sales level must be for total net income for the six-month period (cell I12) to be at least $150. Right now your six-month total is only $138.32, so you know that your January sales must be higher than $100. Although you can solve this particular problem mathematically, you can also solve it fairly quickly by trial and error using this program.

To solve this problem, press the F6 key to put the cursor in the left window. Then move the cursor to cell C5. Enter a new sales figure and press ENTER. Is the resulting total net income figure in cell I12 too high or too low? Enter a new figure in cell C5 to try again. After four or five quick tries you should be reasonably close to the answer. (The answer is that January sales must be at least $104.63 for total net income to be at least $150.)

To demonstrate the Sync subcommand (synchronized windows), move the cursor to the right window. Then move the cursor down to row 25. What happens to the alignment of the rows on the income statement? The right window and the left window scroll together. This is called synchronization. Now type /WWU. This will unsynchronize the two windows. Move the cursor up to row 1 again. The right window scrolls but the left window doesn't.

Type /WWC to eliminate the two windows, and then move the cursor to cell A1.

Status (/WS)

Type /WS now. The result is a status report on all of the Global settings. Although some of the settings are given in code, you can probably decipher them easily. Press the ESC key when you have finished examining this report.

RANGE COMMANDS

Range commands affect specific portions of the worksheet. The subcommands for Erase (/RE), Format (/RF), and Label-Prefix (/RL) have already been discussed. Most of the remaining Range commands will be discussed here. As mentioned in Lesson 1, when prompted by Range commands to specify cells in a range, there are four basic responses:

1. Accept the computer's offer and press ENTER.
2. Point to the range of your choice.
3. Type in the range of your choice.
4. Press ESC or CTRL BREAK to stop the command from being executed.

Name (/RN)

This command allows you to give a range of cells a specific name (e.g., SALES, JEAN, XY). The name may be up to 15 characters long. Later, any time you are asked to enter a range, you may specify the range by typing the name rather than typing the cell references.

To demonstrate the **Range Name** command, type /RN now. Next, type **C** to **C**reate a name, then type the name **SALES**, and press ENTER. To indicate the cells that are included in the range, type **C5.I5** and press ENTER. Now, any time you wish to do something to this group of cells, you can indicate the range by typing the word **SALES** instead of the cell coordinates. As an example, suppose you wish to change the values in that range to integers (Currency format with zero decimal places). Type **/RFC0** and press ENTER. For the range, type **SALES** and press ENTER. The specified cells should now be expressed as integers.

To return the values to their original format, type **/RFC2** and press ENTER. To indicate the range, press the F3 key. In the Control Panel, you now see the name SALES highlighted. If you had previously named other ranges, their names would appear as well. You would move the menu pointer to the proper name and press ENTER. In this case, there is only one name, so just press ENTER. The range named SALES will be put back to its original format. Range names are saved when the file is saved.

Justify (/RJ)

This command is a word processing feature of 1-2-3. Suppose you have typed a paragraph of instructions at the top of a spreadsheet model. Later, you revise the instructions by deleting and adding words, and you end up with a very ragged looking paragraph. You can then use the Range Justify command to reposition the words in the paragraph so that all lines begin at the left side of the range you specify.

Protect (/RP) and Unprotect (/RU)

The Range Protect and Range Unprotect commands are used to protect (or unprotect) specific portions of the worksheet. These commands work only after the Worksheet Global Protection Enable (/WGPE) command has been entered. In other words, the worksheet protection system must be turned on before these two Range subcommands can be used.

Let's work through an example to see how these commands are used. Enter /WGPE to turn on the worksheet protection feature. Move the cursor to cell C4, type the word **PIRATE**, and press ENTER. A noisy little beep and a message in the lower left corner of the screen tell you that this cell is protected; you cannot change its contents. In fact, at this point, all cells are protected. Press ESC or ENTER now to clear your entry.

If you want to answer what-if questions with your model, you will have to unprotect one or more cells so that you can enter proposed changes. On your income statement model, cell C5 is an important cell; if it were unprotected, you could perform what-if analysis. Move the cursor to cell C5, type /RU, and press ENTER to accept the program's range offer. Notice that the cursor in the unprotected cell is highlighted. You can now do what-if analysis by changing the value in C5 without accidentally harming other parts of your model.

In some worksheets there may be several key input cells that you want unprotected. You can unprotect any range of cells in the same way you unprotected the single cell.

After unprotecting a cell, you may find circumstances where you wish to re-protect it. Let's do that with cell C5 now. Move the cursor to cell C5, enter the command /RP, and press ENTER. Cell C5 is now protected again, and you cannot change its contents.

Before moving on to the next section, the entire model should be unprotected so that the subcommands in the remaining sections of this tutorial can be demonstrated. To turn off protection, type the command /WGPD. This disables the protection feature.

You can always check to see whether the protection is off or on by entering the Worksheet Status command. Enter that command now. You should find the word OFF or DISABLED next to Global Protection (or under the word Protect for Version 1A). Then press ESC or ENTER.

MOVE COMMAND (/M)

This command allows you to move a range of cells to another location on the worksheet. Two examples will be provided here. The first example demonstrates moving a range to a blank range. The second example involves moving a range of cells to a range where the cells already contain data.

First, suppose that you want to move the TOTAL column (column I) to the center of the screen below the monthly income statements. Move the cursor to cell I3 and press /M. Now press the Down Arrow key ten times to expand the FROM range from I3 to I13, then press ENTER. The program responds by asking for the range to move TO. Move the cursor to cell E17 and press ENTER again. In a flash, the move is completed! Note that you only had to indicate the beginning cell in the TO range.

Now let's move the TOTAL column back to its original location using the typing method. With the cursor still in cell I3, enter /M, type **E17.E27** as the range to move FROM, and press ENTER. Next, type the beginning cell location of the range to move TO (**I3**). Since the computer is already offering this as a suggestion, simply press ENTER. Instantly, the TOTAL column moves back.

To demonstrate the second kind of move, let's switch GENERAL EXPENSES and SELLING EXPENSES. This will take a little more maneuvering than the previous case because when you move a range to another location, the computer will overwrite the contents of any cells underneath. Move the cursor to cell A7 and insert a blank row (/WIR and press ENTER). This moves SELLING EXPENSES to row 8. Next, move the cursor to cell A9, enter /M, press the Right Arrow key eight times to complete the FROM range, and press ENTER. Then move the cursor up to cell A7 and press ENTER to complete the TO range. Finally, with the cursor still in cell A9, enter /WDR and press ENTER to delete the extra row. The switch is now complete.

It is important to note that all formulas affected by a move are automatically changed by the program.

SYSTEM (/S)

(This command is not available on Version 1A.) This command allows you to exit to DOS without killing the program. You may then execute an operating system command (such as formatting a new disk), and, when done, type the word **EXIT**, and return to the Lotus 1-2-3 program exactly where you left it.

SUMMARY

The goal of Lesson 1 and Lesson 2 has been to introduce you to the important features of Lotus 1-2-3 and its command structure. You have covered a great deal of territory in these first two lessons. With practice, you should be able to use this knowledge to modify and manipulate spreadsheet models created by someone else. You should also be able to design and develop some rather sophisticated spreadsheet models of your own. Again, as at the end of Lesson 1, you are encouraged to review Appendix B of this workbook for advice on resolving common problems incurred when working with Lotus 1-2-3.

LESSON 3

GRAPHICS

Learning Objectives

Topics introduced in this lesson are:

- constructing graphs (Graph commands)
- exploring graph options
- naming graphs for later recall
- what-if graphing
- saving graphs to be printed
- printing graphs (PrintGraph commands)

Lotus 1-2-3 allows the user to view worksheet data graphically on the screen and to print graphs. These are very exciting features of Lotus 1-2-3, but not all IBM PC's have the capability of displaying or printing graphics. You need both a graphics display screen and a graphics card installed in the computer to view graphs on the screen. You must have a printer with graphics capabilities to print the graphs. You do not need a color monitor or a color printer (plotter). As with the Print command, you also need Lotus 1-2-3 disks with the correct hardware configuration recorded on them. See your instructor if you have any questions about proper configuration of your disks.

The commands which put graphs on your screen are called **Graph** commands. They are accessed from the Lotus 1-2-3 System Disk. Printing a graph on the printer requires a Lotus 1-2-3 disk called the PrintGraph Disk.

GRAPH COMMANDS (/G)

The **Graph** commands allow you to display spreadsheet figures graphically on your screen. If you are unsure how your machine is configured, you may try the steps outlined in this section anyway. When you get to the final step, if the Mode Indicator flashes WAIT for several seconds or your screen goes blank, your IBM PC is not equipped to handle graphics. You should then press ESC to kill the command and go on to the next lesson.

In this lesson, you will be dealing with the file named LESSON3. Please load it now from your Template Disk (**/FR LESSON3**). The file LESSON3 should appear as shown in Illustration 8.

Illustration 8
Income Statement Saved
as File LESSON3

```
A1:                                                              READY

        A       B       C        D        E        F        G        H
1
2                           Easy Over Inc.
3                         Net Income Projection
4
5                         Jan      Feb      Mar      Apr      May      Jun
6                       -------  -------  -------  -------  -------  -------
7       Sales          $100.00  $102.00  $104.04  $106.12  $108.24  $110.41
8
9       Selling expenses $60.00   $61.20   $62.42   $63.67   $64.95   $66.24
10      General expenses  19.00    19.00    19.00    19.00    19.00    19.00
11                       -------  -------  -------  -------  -------  -------
12      Total expenses   $79.00   $80.20   $81.42   $82.67   $83.95   $85.24
13                       -------  -------  -------  -------  -------  -------
14      Net income       $21.00   $21.80   $22.62   $23.45   $24.30   $25.16
15                       =======  =======  =======  =======  =======  =======
16
17
18
19
20
```

Constructing Graphs

The Graph commands are extensive, so all that will be attempted here is to expose you to some basic commands. Let's develop a line graph comparing sales and total expenses for the six months. When you are done, the graph on the screen should appear as shown in Illustration 9. To activate the graph commands, type /G (Graph). (On Version 2.2, a Graph Settings sheet will appear on the screen. The settings sheet display can be turned off and on by pressing the F6 key.) From the menu of subcommands, select T (Type). As you see from the next submenu, a line graph is one of several graph options. All the graph types will be explored later, but for now type L (Line). Next, you should specify the X-axis range. From the menu of subcommands, select X. You are asked to enter the X-axis range. Move the cursor to cell C5 (Jan), press the Period (.) key, press the Right Arrow key five times to expand the range to cell H5 (Jun), and press ENTER.

Now you need to enter the sales and total expense data on the graph. There are six data-ranges (specified as A through F) that can be entered on a graph. In your graph, one data-range (A) will be "sales," and another data-range (B) will be "total expenses." To enter these data-ranges now, from the menu of subcommands, select A. You are asked to enter the first data-range. Move the cursor to cell C7, press the Period key, press the Right Arrow key five times to expand the range to cell H7, and press ENTER. Finally, from the menu of subcommands, select B. You are asked to enter the second data-range. Move the cursor to cell C12, press the Period key, press the Right Arrow key five times to expand the range to cell H12, and press ENTER.

From the menu of subcommands, select V for View. What you should see now is a line graph plotting monthly sales and expenses. There are no titles or legends on this graph (these will be added later), but the X-axis and the two data-ranges should appear as in Illustration 9.

Each data-range has its own symbols as shown in the chart below (data-ranges C through F are not used in this graph):

Data Range	Symbol
A	square
B	cross
C	diamond
D	triangle
E	X
F	upside-down triangle

Now let's look at some other types of graphs. Press ESC or ENTER to return to the graph submenu, press T (Type), select P (Pie), and type V (View). On pie graphs, the X-axis is used to

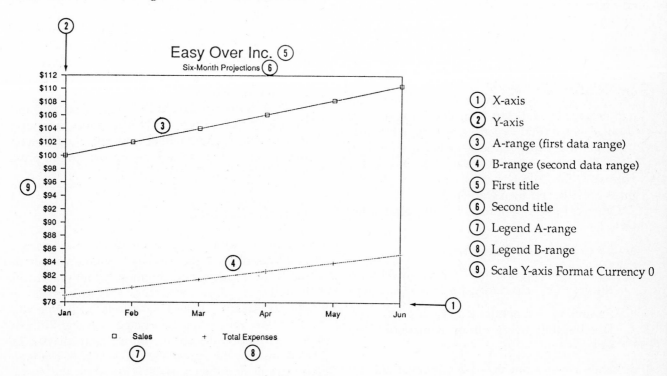

Illustration 9 Line graph plotting monthly sales and expenses

describe the pieces of the pie, and the A-range numbers are used in computing the proportionate size of each slice. Pie graphs do not include more than one data-range. When done viewing the pie graph, try the Bar graph and then the Stacked-Bar graph. These are self-explanatory.

Finally, try the XY graph. This graph is commonly called a scattergraph. With the current graph specifications, you will not see much on the screen when you try the XY option because this graph type requires that the X-axis be values, not labels. For example, you might use an XY graph to show the relationship between monthly units sold and monthly advertising costs. To do this, you might enter monthly units sales in column B of your template and monthly advertising costs in column C. To plot this data as an XY graph, you would use column B as the X-axis and column C as the A-range. You will have the opportunity to try some XY graphs as you complete the problems in the workbook. However, for now, reset the Type to Line graph before continuing on to the next section.

Graph Options

To explore some helpful options to "dress up" your line graph, press **O** to select the Options subcommand from the Graph menu. Let's begin by putting a title at the top of the graph. Type **T** for **Titles**, **F** for **First**, type **Easy Over Inc.**, and press ENTER. Select **T** for Titles, **S** for Second, type **Six-Month Projections**, and press ENTER.

Next, let's use legends to identify the data-ranges. Type **L** for Legend, **A** for A-range, enter **Sales**, and press ENTER. Select **L** for Legend again, **B** for B-range, enter **Total Expenses**, and press ENTER.

To get the Y-axis values expressed with dollar signs ($) in front, type **S** for Scale, **Y** for Y-axis, **F** for Format, **C** for Currency, **0** for zero decimal places, press ENTER, and then **Q** to Quit.

Other common options not demonstrated here include:

a. Titles X-axis and Titles Y-axis

b. Grid — puts vertical and/or horizontal lines on the graph to help clarify the data point values.

c. Scale Skip — unclutters a crowded X-axis by labeling only every nth coordinate on the X-axis.

d. Scale Y-axis Manual — 1-2-3 automatically sets the scale displayed on the Y-axis based on the

values found in the data-ranges. If this is not acceptable to the graph designer, the automatic scale can be manually overridden specifying the lower and upper limits. This option does not work with bar graphs.

e. Color — displays the graph in color if you have a color monitor.

Press **Q** to Quit the Options submenu and press **V** to View the results of you efforts. The graph should appear as in Illustration 9. When done viewing the graph, press ENTER to get back to the graph menu.

Naming and Recalling Graphs

You may wish to retain several different graphs for a single worksheet. Once the basic graphics options have been selected for each graph, you can name each graph to keep it for immediate access at a later point in time. For example, to name your line graph type **N** for Name and **C** for Create. Type the name **LNGR** and press ENTER. If you had other graphs you wished to keep, you would give them different names. Press **Q** to Quit the graph menu now.

As with range names, graph names are saved when the file is saved. Type **/FS**, and the computer offers the file name LESSON3. With Versions 2, 2.01, and 2.2, the computer adds the suffix .WK1; this is OK, press ENTER to accept it. With Version 1A, press ENTER to accept the name offered and then press **R** to indicate you wish to Replace the old file with the new.

Now to call up the graph LNGR, type **/GN** and then **U** for Use. Press ENTER to select the graph named LNGR, and it will be immediately drawn on the screen. When done viewing the graph, press ENTER and **Q** to Quit.

What-If Graphing

There is a fast way to recall the most recent graph used. Press the F10 key any time you are in the READY mode, and the most recent graph will be redisplayed on the screen. This feature allows you to perform "what-if" graphing. Each time you enter new values in a data-range, pressing F10 will let you graphically see the impact immediately. To demonstrate this, press the F10 key now, examine the graph, and then press ENTER. Move the cursor to cell C7, enter **45**, and press ENTER again. Press the F10 key now and note how the graph has been redrawn to accept the new input. Press ENTER and feel free to experiment with other values entered in cell C7. Reset cell C7 to **100** when done.

Saving Graphs (for Printing)

Lotus 1-2-3 has a special program which will allow you to print out graphs on your printer. Printing graphs is a fairly simple process, but it cannot be done with worksheet files. It will only work with special "picture" files. Converting a worksheet file to a picture file is easily done with the **Graph Save** command. The program will save the most recent graph drawn as a picture file. In your case, this is the line graph from LESSON3. Since this graph is still in memory, type /G for **Graph** and S for **Save**. Then type the name **LES-SON3G** and press ENTER. Your graph is now saved as a picture (PIC) file. Press **Q** to Quit.

Please note that the **Graph Save** command is used for entirely different purposes than the **Graph Name** command. The **Graph Save** command saves graphs for printing on the printer. The **Graph Name** command saves graphs for viewing on the screen. One command is not dependent on the other.

PRINTGRAPH

To print out your PIC file, you will need to use a disk called the Lotus 1-2-3 PrintGraph Disk. This is a separate disk from the Lotus 1-2-3 System Disk and must be obtained from your instructor. Do not continue with this lesson until this disk is available to you. Assuming that you have just finished saving the PIC file called LESSON3G and are in the READY mode, press /QY to quit the spreadsheet portion of 1-2-3. With Version 2.2, press **Y** one more time to end. The next screen is the 1-2-3 Access System Menu. Type **P** to select PrintGraph and insert the PrintGraph Disk when requested. The Print-Graph commands vary between Version 1A and Version 2. Follow the instructions below for the version which you are using.

Version 1A

The PrintGraph main menu options appear as follows:

Select Options Go Configure Align Page Quit

Below the control panel are listed several groups of configuration options. Of immediate concern to you are the listings under Directories. The directory under Pictures should be B:\, and the directory under Fonts should be A:\. If either of these directories is incorrect, it must be changed.[1]

Next, examine the listing under Graphics Device. If your printer make is not listed there, this must be corrected.[2]

If the Graphics Device and the Directories are correct, press **S** from the main menu to Select a picture file. The files list is then presented to you. In this case, there is only one file on it--LESSON3G. Press ENTER to select it. Turn your printer on and press **G** to Go. After a short wait, the printer should spring into action. Graphics printing is much slower than text printing. The printer may spit out several blank lines before printing the graph.

After a few minutes, the graph will be done. Press *P* to eject the page. If you want to show off your graph, turn off the computer and remove your disks. If you want to return to the Lotus 1-2-3 program, press **Q** to Quit the PrintGraph Program and then remove the PrintGraph Disk. Reinsert the Lotus 1-2-3 System Disk and press ENTER.

Versions 2, 2.01, and 2.2

The PrintGraph main menu options appear as follows:

Image-Select Settings Go Align Page Exit

Below the Control Panel are listed several groups of configuration options. Of immediate concern to you are the listings under Hardware. The directory under Graphs should be B:\, and the directory

---

[1] To change directories, remove the write-protect tab from your disk if necessary, and type **C** for **Configure** and **F** for **Files**. Then type **P** for Pictures (or **F** for Fonts) and press the ESC key. Type **B:** (or **A:**) and press ENTER. (Either capital or lowercase letters are acceptable.) Insert the disk when requested and press ENTER again. Press **Q** when done and then press **S** to Save this configuration. Finally, press **Q** to get back to the main PrintGraph menu.

[2] To reconfigure the PrintGraph Disk for your printer, remove the write-protect tab from your disk if necessary, and press **C** for **Configure** and then **D** for **Device**. Follow the instructions on the screen to select your printer. Then press **S** to Save this configuration. Finally, press **Q** to return to the main PrintGraph menu.

under Fonts should be A:\. If either of these directories is incorrect, it must be changed.[3]

Next, examine the printer listed under Hardware. If your printer make is not listed there, this must be corrected.[4]

If the Printer and the Hardware are correct, press **I** from the main menu to Image-Select a picture file. The files list is then presented to you. In this case, there is only one file on it--LESSON3G. Press the Spacebar to mark the graph and then press ENTER to select it. After selecting the file, with Version 2.2, you may press the F10 key to preview the graph on the screen before printing it. Turn your printer on and press **G** to Go. After a short wait, the printer should spring into action. Graphics printing is much slower than text printing. The printer may spit out several blank lines before printing the graph.

After a few minutes, the graph will be done. Press **P** to eject the page. If you want to show off your graph, turn off the computer and remove the disks. If you want to return to the Lotus 1-2-3 program, press **EY** to exit the PrintGraph Program. Remove the PrintGraph Disk. Reinsert the Lotus 1-2-3 System Disk and press ENTER. At the A prompt, type **LOTUS** to return to the 1-2-3 Access System Menu.

---

[3] To change directories, remove the write-protect tab from your disk if necessary, type **S** for Settings, **H** for Hardware, **G** for Graphs Directory (or **F** for Fonts), and press the ESC key. Type **B:** (or **A:**) and press ENTER. (Either capital or lowercase letters are acceptable.) Insert the disk when requested and press ENTER again. Press **Q** when done and then press **S** to Save this configuration. The program will automatically return you to the PrintGraph menu.

[4] To reconfigure the PrintGraph Disk for your printer, remove the write-protect tab from your disk if necessary, press **S** for Settings, **H** for Hardware, and then **P** for Printer. Follow the instructions on the screen to select your printer. After the printer is selected, press **Q** for Quit. Then press **S** to Save this configuration.

LESSON 4

MACROS

Learning Objectives

Topics included in this lesson are:

- definition of a macro
- developing and saving macros
- sample designs for go-to, print, and save macros
- debugging techniques

One of the more advanced features of Lotus 1-2-3 is its ability to execute user-created keyboard commands. This is commonly referred to as a keyboard memory feature or, simply, a macro. Macros are activated by pressing the ALT key and a letter key. On Version 2.2, you may also use the ALT key and the F3 key to activate a macro. Macros can be used to automatically print files, format ranges, combine files, move the cursor to a specified cell, set up a user-created menu system, and so forth. Virtually every keystroke and command you can type on the keyboard can be embedded in a macro.

DEVELOPING AND SAVING MACROS

A macro is entered as a label in a cell (or series of cells). Keys with special names must be entered in brackets. For example, the Up Arrow key, the HOME key, and the F5 (Go To) key would be entered as {UP}, {HOME}, and {GOTO}, respectively. Other keys are entered directly. Note that the bracket symbols, {}, are used. Do not confuse these with the parentheses, (), or the braces, [].

To demonstrate how a macro is created and executed, let's develop a simple macro for your file LESSON1. Load that file now (/**FR LESSON1**). The file LESSON1 should appear as shown in Illustration 10.

Let's develop a macro for this model which will automatically enter 100 in cell C7 whenever you want.

To begin, move the cursor to cell C7 and change it from 100 to **110**. After pressing ENTER, move the cursor to cell B30.

Illustration 10
Income Statement Saved as File
LESSON1

```
A1:                                                              READY

        A        B        C        D        E        F        G        H
 1
 2                           Easy Over Inc.
 3                        Net Income Projection
 4
 5                         Jan      Feb      Mar      Apr      May      Jun
 6                       -------  -------  -------  -------  -------  -------
 7   Sales              $100.00  $102.00  $104.04  $106.12  $108.24  $110.41
 8
 9   Selling expenses    $60.00   $61.20   $62.42   $63.67   $64.95   $66.24
10   General expenses     19.00    19.00    19.00    19.00    19.00    19.00
11                       -------  -------  -------  -------  -------  -------
12   Total expenses      $79.00   $80.20   $81.42   $82.67   $83.95   $85.24
13                       -------  -------  -------  -------  -------  -------
14   Net income          $21.00   $21.80   $22.62   $23.45   $24.30   $25.16
15                       =======  =======  =======  =======  =======  =======
16
17
18
19
20
```

If you were now asked to move back to cell C7 and reset it to 100, you could use the F5 key (Go To) to do so. The following keystrokes are needed to move the cursor to C7 and enter 100. Try it.

F5 (Goto)
C
7
ENTER
1
0
0
ENTER

Now let's put this in the form of a macro. Change C7 from 100 back to 110 again and move the cursor to cell B30. (Typically, macros are hidden off-screen so that they do not confuse users.) First, unprotect the worksheet by entering **/WGPD** (Worksheet Global Protection Disable). Then, type **{GOTO}C7~100~** and press ENTER. Remember, both capital and lowercase letters will do. The Tilde (~) symbol stands for the ENTER key. If you make a mistake entering the macro, edit your entry using the F2 key.

You have just typed a macro, but it needs a name before it can work. With the cursor still in cell B30, enter the following:

1. **/R** for Range
2. **N** for Name
3. **C** for Create
4. **\J** for the name. For 1-2-3 versions prior to 2.2, all macro names must begin with the Backslash key (\) and be followed by a single letter. (Note: You must use the Backslash (\) key; not the Slash (/) key.) With Version 2.2, multiple-character names can be used (i.e., JUMP_C7).
5. Press ENTER to end the name.
6. Press ENTER to accept the range designation.

Your macro is now complete. To use it, hold down the ALT key and press the J key. If you have done everything correctly, the cursor should jump to cell C7 and enter 100. This macro will work no matter where the cursor is. Feel free to experiment with this macro if you wish. Under Version 2.2, if you use the multiple-character macro name, the macro is run by holding down the ALT key, pressing the F3 key, and selecting the macro name.

It is a good habit to leave the macro name in the cell just to the left of where the macro itself is entered. Do this now by moving the cursor to cell A30 and typing **macro J** (or just **J** or **'\J**). This is particularly needed when you have a spreadsheet model with several macros.

A macro may extend downward from the original cell. For example, if you wished to add some additional steps to your J macro, you could tack them on to the end of what you have already entered in cell B30, or you could put the additional steps in cell B31. A macro stops executing when it moves down a column and reaches a blank cell. Also, if you ever get stuck in a macro, use the CTRL key, BRK key combination to stop the macro.

Before going further, save your J macro now by saving this modified template as LESSON1. Type **/FS**, and the computer offers the file name LESSON1. With Versions 2, 2.01, and 2.2, the computer adds the suffix .WK1; this is OK, press ENTER to accept it. With Version 1A, press ENTER to accept the name offered and then press **R** to indicate you wish to replace the old file with the new.

SAMPLE MACRO DESIGNS

Below are some other sample macros you may want to try with LESSON1.

Keystrokes	Result
{HOME}{GOTO}C7~100~	Pulls column A and row 1 onto the screen before moving to cell C7 and entering 100. This could be named \A.
{HOME}{LEFT}{LEFT} {GOTO}C7~100~	Same as above, with sound effects (in cell A1, the Left Arrow key will cause the computer to beep twice). This macro could be named \B.
'/PPRA1.H15~AGPQ	Prints spreadsheet. The apostrophe at the beginning is to invoke the LABEL mode. It will not show up on the screen. The rest stands for each keystroke needed to print the spreadsheet. This follows the exact sequence used to demonstrate the printing command in Lesson 1: /Print Printer Range **A1.H15** ENTER Align Go Page Quit. A common name used for a print macro is \P.
'/FSLESSON1~R	Saves updated version of LESSON1. This one could be named \S.

DEBUGGING TECHNIQUES

When developing a macro on your own, first write down on a piece of paper the exact keystrokes you would enter to execute the desired command sequence. Then type the macro in a cell (or cells) on the template and name it.

Very frequently, macros that you are creating do not work on the first try and must be "debugged" before they execute properly. To determine where the error is, carefully go over the macro one character at a time. If necessary, type the desired command sequence and compare it keystroke for keystroke to the macro you have written. Characters frequently forgotten are the Apostrophe ('), Slash (/), Tilde (~), and Q (to quit). Other errors may be things like using an O instead of a 0 (zero) or forgetting to use the Backslash key when naming the macro range. In some cases, you may also need to undo the effects of the erroneous commands executed by the errant macro before trying a corrected macro. One of the best ways to "restore" a template is to write a macro, save the file, and then test the macro. If the macro does not work properly, retrieve the "clean" file, debug the macro, save the file, and attempt the macro again. This is especially useful when the macro involves several steps.

With Versions 2, 2.01, and 2.2, there is a STEP mode that can be used to run a macro one keystroke at a time. It is turned on (and off) by holding down the ALT key and pressing the F2 key. Once in the STEP Mode, activate a macro, and then press the Spacebar to execute the macro keystroke by keystroke. This feature is very helpful when trying to locate errors in macros.

With Version 2.2, there is also a LEARN Mode that can be used to create a macro. To use this mode, first enter the command /Worksheet Learn Range (/WLR) and specify a range of blank cells where a macro can be entered. Then hold down the ALT key and press the F5 key to turn on the LEARN Mode. Once in this mode, every key you type will be recorded in the Learn Range as a label. When you have finished all the keystrokes in the macro, hold down the ALT key and press F5 to exit the LEARN Mode. The macro would then be named and run in the same way as other macros.

If you tried any of the macros listed above and want to save them, be sure to save your updated version of LESSON1 . If you wrote and executed the macro named \S, the updated version of LESSON1 has already been saved.

Macros are most helpful when they are created to substitute for keystrokes and commands you frequently use. They can also be used to develop elaborate and sophisticated spreadsheet models. For the advanced programmer, there are many additional macro commands which are beyond the scope of the tutorial.

LESSON 5
MODEL-BUILDING HINTS

Learning Objectives

Topics included in this lesson are:
- planning and design concerns
- documentation suggestions
- "direct entry" vs. "data section" approaches
- protecting your worksheets

The term "model-building" may sound highly technical and sophisticated, but this is not necessarily the case with spreadsheet models. Although elaborate and complex spreadsheet models can be designed to handle everything from detailed investment analysis to complex engineering applications, spreadsheet models can also be developed to solve simple problems too. As you saw in Lesson 2, the six-month income statement projection was an elementary yet flexible model, and it was fairly easy to design and use.

Lesson 5 provides general recommendations on model-building techniques. Suggestions for constructing and documenting spreadsheet models are stressed. Each time you begin building a model, you may want to review these suggestions.

1. Planning saves time and trouble. Although there are many ways to correct design problems with spreadsheet models (e.g., Insert, Delete, Move), much time will be saved if you lay out a tentative structure for the model on paper before turning the computer on.
   Particular attention should be given to global formats and alignment. These should be entered on the worksheet before any entries are made. You can always override the Global commands later (with Range commands) if specific cells require special formatting or alignment.
2. Use all available resources. When you have a question, don't hesitate to examine the manual which accompanies the 1-2-3 program. There is also a multitude of reference books on 1-2-3 modeling available in bookstores and libraries.
3. Document your worksheet. You should design your model so that six months from now you

can remember the purpose of the template and how it works.

a. Choose a file name for your model that is both descriptive and simple. This will help eliminate the frustration of typing incorrect file names when loading your model.
b. You may wish to put a short written description of what the model does on the worksheet.
c. Where appropriate, include important instructions and explanatory notes on the face of the worksheet.
d. Clearly indicate on the worksheet the assumptions that underlie any calculations. An easy way to accomplish this is to include a Data Section, which isolates all relevant assumptions and variables in one spot on the model. A Data Section should always be given strong consideration since it helps highlight the numerical assumptions of the model, and it facilitates performing what-if analysis.

Without a Data Section, labels, data, and/or formulas would be entered directly in the template at appropriate locations. If new information is provided, the new labels, data, and/or formulas will be reentered directly into the model. This "direct-entry" model is an acceptable design if the changeable information is data or labels only. It is generally inefficient and cumbersome if the change in data involves revising formulas.

With a Data Section, all of the input data will be placed in one spot on the template, and all formulas in the answer will reference the appropriate cells in the Data Section. If new information is provided, changes are made to the Data Section only. No formulas need to be revised.

Review Illustration 2 in Lesson 1 on page 10. It is an example of a "direct-entry" type model. There are four assumptions in the model: January sales are $100, sales growth rate is 2% per month, selling expenses are 60% of sales, and general expenses are $19 per month. Because just about every cell other than C7 (January sales) has formulas in it, a change in any assumption other than the January sales level would require revising formulas. For example, if selling expenses were changed to 55% of sales, the formulas in six cells (C9 through H9) would have to be rewritten.

Now load the file LESSON5 from the Template Disk (**/FR LESSON5**). It should appear as shown in Illustration 11. This is an example of a model using a Data Section. Note that the four assumptions of the model are listed in the Data Section, and they are the only cells unprotected. Move the cursor to the Answer Section and examine the contents of the cells. Note that they contain formulas that use cell references from the Data Section. Thus, any time you enter new values in the Data Section, the Answer Section recalculates a new answer without having to redo the formulas. As a result of its design, this model is extremely flexible and offers excellent opportunities for performing what-if analysis. Move the cursor to the Data Section and insert a variety of values for each

input. Note the changes in the Net Income Projection statement.

4. Pay attention to alignment and format. Put labels over all columns. Use the currency and comma formats where appropriate. Use an integer format (no decimal places) where decimal accuracy is not needed. Use standard accounting conventions, such as rules, double rules, and accepted abbreviations, whenever appropriate. Use uppercase and lowercase letters just as you would in a handwritten or typed report. Your model may perform a sophisticated analysis, but if it is cluttered and difficult to read, no one will appreciate your brilliance.

5. When printing your model, you do not have to print all cells used to calculate your answer. It is a common practice to place "scratch pads" and tables out of sight if they clutter up your printout or do not provide useful information to the template user.

6. Beware of being too comprehensive. It may be easy to develop a template which handles a specific set of facts, but it may be difficult to modify that template to encompass other facts and circumstances. Do not always attempt to

Illustration 11
Income Statement Model
with Data Section
(Rows 1 Through 20)

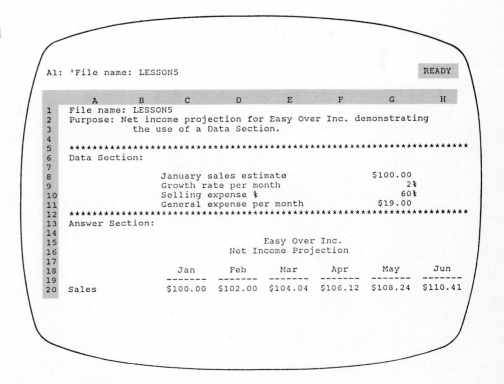

cover all possibilities with one single model. For example, it may be easier to develop several different depreciation calculation models than it would be to develop a single model that covers all methods.

7. Always keep flexibility in mind. One of the most powerful features of a spreadsheet program is its ability to perform instant recalculations when new data are entered. This ability is enhanced if your models are designed to accept new input without having to alter previously entered formulas. This is another important reason to use a Data Section at the top of the worksheet.

8. Learn to use the Copy command. This command was discussed on page 17. It can be used frequently when setting up many spreadsheet models. It will save much time and trouble once you get used to it. If you make a mistake when copying, simply do it over. Try it; practice makes perfect!

9. Don't be afraid to use the special function commands discussed in Appendix C. The @IF function may scare you, but it looks harder than it really is. The @IF function can add a great deal of power and flexibility to your models. The same is true of the **@HLOOKUP** and **@VLOOKUP** commands. You can begin to develop very sophisticated spreadsheet models when you learn to use these commands.

10. In general, if you develop a model with a Data Section, you should enter some sample data before programming your answer. Developing a "blank" spreadsheet model with correct formulas and format is quite difficult.

11. Protect your worksheet from hardware and software failures. Also, protect your worksheet from accidental changes.

   a. Always keep a printout of the model on file. Should you ever lose or destroy a model saved on a disk, you can reconstruct it much faster by looking at a printout of the original.

   b. Keep a printout of the "cell contents" on file. Obtaining a printout of cell contents was discussed in Lesson 1.

   c. Keep a backup copy of your model on a disk separate from the one you stored the original model on.

   d. As you are developing a model, save it on disk at frequent intervals.

   e. Use the Worksheet and Range Protect options to prevent mistaken entry into or erasure of important cells.

   f. After saving a model, always check the files list (/FLW) to see that your new file is included.

Model building can be simplified and more creative if these suggestions are followed. You are certain to enjoy developing your own spreadsheet models, but don't be surprised if it's harder than it looks!

INSTRUCTIONS FOR SAMPLE PROBLEMS

There are two sets of problems contained in this workbook: preprogrammed and model-building. With the preprogrammed problems, you will complete spreadsheet models that have already been set up for you. You must finish the template, experiment with the results, and then answer several questions to complete each assignment. The basic instructions for completing preprogrammed problems are found in Sample 1.

Each preprogrammed problem has three optional sections at the end. They are called "Template Tickler," "Graphics Tickler," and "Macro Tickler." Solving the ticklers involve invoking 1-2-3 commands to physically alter the appearance and/or components of the current model. In order to solve the Template Ticklers, you will need some familiarity with spreadsheet modeling concepts and a basic understanding of 1-2-3 commands. These are covered in Lesson 2. A sample Template Tickler is worked in Sample 2. Lesson 3 and Sample 3 serve as preparation for the Graphics Ticklers. Lesson 4 and Sample 4 provide the background to answer the Macro Ticklers.

With the model-building problems, you must develop models from start to finish. These problems are generally not complex, but they take as long to complete as the preprogrammed problems because you have to design the whole template model yourself. Lesson 5 contains hints for completing the model-building problems, and a sample model-building problem is worked in Sample 5.

SAMPLE 1

SAMPLE PREPROGRAMMED PROBLEM

This sample problem is designed to acquaint you with the procedures used to solve the preprogrammed problems in this workbook. Each problem covers a different conceptual area. The problems are equivalent in length to standard homework problems. Initially the problems may require a little more time than regular homework, since you still may be somewhat unfamiliar with Lotus 1-2-3. Once you begin to feel comfortable with the spreadsheet program, however, your problem assignments should go relatively quickly.

The Template Disk provided with this workbook contains a spreadsheet file for each preprogrammed problem. Each file is a spreadsheet model (template) that is generally divided into two sections: a Data Section and an Answer Section. The Data Section contains the quantitative information needed to solve the problem. The Answer Section provides the basic format for your solution.

The preprogrammed problems have the following parts: the problem statement, the problem requirements, a printout of the template, and the template itself, which is found on the Template Disk. The general procedures for solving the problems will be explained in the following paragraphs, using a sample problem. The sample problem appears in the boxed areas on the following pages.

First, read the problem statement shown in Illustration 12 on the next page. Then, read the first problem requirement shown in Illustration 13 on the next page. This requirement states the basic aim of the problem and asks you to review the printout of the template.

A printout of the template is found at the end of each problem. The template printout for the sample program is shown in Illustration 14 on the next page.

Notice the following features of the template:

1. In the upper left corner of the worksheet, you will see the file name SAMPLE. You should always check the file name to see that you have loaded the correct template into the computer.
2. The columns and rows in the work area of the template are labeled in column A and in row 4. This is a convenience for you so that when the

Salyers Enterprises Inc. is interested in estimating net income for each of the next five months. It appears that January sales will be $10,000 and the company is hopeful that sales will increase by 2% per month. Selling expenses are roughly 60% of each month's sales, and general expenses average $1,900 each month.

Illustration 12   Sample Problem Statement

Required

1) You have been asked by Salyers Enterprises to provide net income projections for the next 5 months. Review the printed template called SAMPLE. Note that the problem data have already been entered into the Data Section of the template. Note also that the basic format for the solution has been set up in the Answer Section.

Illustration 13   Sample Problem Requirement 1

```
SAMPLE                  Student Name    =>
                        Section Number  =>
--------------------------------------------------------------------
A      B        C        D        E        F        G        H
--------------------------------------------------------------------
 6 Data Section:
 7
 8              January sales              $10,000
 9              Sales growth rate              2%
10              Selling expense ratio         60%
11              General expenses          $1,900
12 -----------------------------------------------------------------
13 Answer Section:
14
15                      Jan      Feb      Mar      Apr      May
16                      -------  -------  -------  -------  -------
17 Sales               FORMULA1 FORMULA2      $0       $0       $0
18
19 Selling expenses    FORMULA3      $0       $0       $0       $0
20 General expenses    FORMULA4       0        0        0        0
21                      -------  -------  -------  -------  -------
22 Total expenses      FORMULA5      $0       $0       $0       $0
23                      -------  -------  -------  -------  -------
24 Net income          FORMULA6      $0       $0       $0       $0
25                      =======  =======  =======  =======  =======
26 -----------------------------------------------------------------
```

Illustration 14   Template Printout

38

worksheet is printed out, you will be able to locate specific cell coordinates quickly. This will be particularly helpful when discussing problem solutions in class.

3. The work area of the template is divided into two sections: the Data Section and the Answer Section.

4. Values in the Data and Answer Sections are formatted using the appropriate formatting options.

5. The Answer Section contains several cells labeled FORMULA1, FORMULA2, etc. This indicates the cells in which you will be entering your formulas to solve the problem.

The next step is to write the formulas. Requirement 2, shown in Illustration 15, asks you to develop the necessary formulas. The formulas and an explanation of each formula are shown after the illustration. Use the information in the Data Section of the template to develop these formulas. Wherever possible, formulas should incorporate cell references rather than specific values. The importance of this will be seen when you perform the what-if analysis in Requirement 4. Write the formulas in the spaces provided in Illustration 15.

The formulas for the sample problems are below.

FORMULA1: +F8

Comment on Formula 1: January sales are given in cell F8 in the Data Section. This formula tells 1-2-3 to use the value found in cell F8 as January sales in the Answer Section of the template.

FORMULA2: +F8*(1+F9) or +F8+F8*F9 or +D17*(1+F9)

Comment on Formula 2: Any of these formulas will do. These formulas will calculate February sales as a 2% increase over January sales. March, April, and May sales are already preprogrammed

in the template. Note that you have expressed the growth rate as a cell reference (F9). This allows you to change the growth rate simply by changing the number in cell F9 rather than by redoing the formula in cell E19. What-if analysis with different growth rates can be performed very quickly this way.

FORMULA3: +F8*F10 or +D17*F10

Comment on Formula 3: According to the assumption in the problem, selling expenses are 60% of sales. Since January sales are already given in cell F8 (or cell D17) and the selling expense ratio is given in cell F10, you can simply multiply the two to compute total selling expenses for the month of January.

FORMULA4: +F11

Comment on Formula 4: General expenses are given in the Data Section in cell F11. This formula tells 1-2-3 to take the value found in cell F11 and place it in cell D20.

FORMULA5: +D19+D20 or @SUM(D19.D20)

Comment on Formula 5: Total expenses are the sum of the selling and general expenses. The @SUM function was discussed on page 8 in Lesson 1.

FORMULA6: +D17-D22

Comment on Formula 6: Net income is the difference between sales and expenses.

After you have written the formulas in the workbook, the next requirement will ask you to load the proper template file and enter the required information. You will also generally be asked to print your completed worksheet using a special print macro. Read Requirement 3 shown in Illustration 16 on the next page and follow the steps listed below to complete the requirement.

2) There are 6 formulas requested in the Answer Section to complete the template. Using the spaces provided below, write the formulas required to complete the template.

FORMULA1_____   FORMULA4_____

FORMULA2_____   FORMULA5_____

FORMULA3_____   FORMULA6_____

Illustration 15 Sample Problem Requirement 2

> 3) Load the spreadsheet program and then load the template SAMPLE from the Template Disk. Enter the 6 formulas in the appropriate cells. Save your solution as SAMPLE3. Use ALT P to print the template when done. (*Check figure: January net income (cell D24), $2,100*)

Illustration 16   Sample Problem Requirement 3

1. Use the DOS and Lotus 1-2-3 System disks to load Lotus 1-2-3 in drive A. Insert the Template Disk into disk drive B. (If your computer has a hard disk drive, see the footnote below.)[1]
2. After Lotus 1-2-3 has been loaded and you are staring at a blank worksheet, type **/FR SAMPLE** to load the proper file.
3. Check the file name printed in cell A1 to make sure you have loaded the correct template. If you have loaded the wrong file, try again.
4. Move the cursor to cell F1 and enter your name. Next, type your section number in cell F2.
5. Enter the six formulas required to complete the template. All the cells that already have numbers or zeros in them have been preprogrammed with the correct formulas. To enter the required formulas, move the cursor to the appropriate cells and type the formulas you

wrote in Requirement 2. For example, to enter FORMULA1, move the cursor to cell D17 and type **+F8**. As you type these formulas, you will see the rest of the template fill in with numbers. Notice that the figures are automatically expressed as integers. When you have entered these formulas, the result should be as shown in Illustration 17.

---

1 The preprogrammed problems in this workbook require that the Template Disk be used in drive A or drive B. Furthermore, the Lotus 1-2-3 Program must be configured to look for this disk in the appropriate drive (referred to as the default drive). Before continuing with this sample problem, type **/WGDD**. If the directory is set at A:\ or B:\, this is okay. Just press ENTER and then **Q** to Quit. If the current directory is set at anything else, press the ESC key and enter **A:** or **B:** whichever is appropriate. Then press ENTER and **Q** to Quit.

Illustration 17
Screen Display of
Completed Template
(lines 6 through 25)

```
B25:                                                              READY

       A      B        C         D        E        F        G        H
  6     6 Data Section:
  7     7
  8     8           January sales            $10,000
  9     9           Sales growth rate             2%
 10    10           Selling expense ratio        60%
 11    11           General expenses         $1,900
 12    12   ----------------------------------------------------------
 13    13 Answer Section:
 14    14
 15    15                        Jan      Feb      Mar      Apr      May
 16    16                      -------  -------  -------  -------  -------
 17    17 Sales               $10,000  $10,200  $10,404  $10,612  $10,824
 18    18
 19    19 Selling expenses     $6,000   $6,120   $6,242   $6,367   $6,495
 20    20 General expenses      1,900    1,900    1,900    1,900    1,900
 21    21                      -------  -------  -------  -------  -------
 22    22 Total expenses       $7,900   $8,020   $8,142   $8,267   $8,395
 23    23                      -------  -------  -------  -------  -------
 24    24 Net income           $2,100   $2,180   $2,262   $2,345   $2,430
 25    25                      =======  =======  =======  =======  =======
```

6. Check figures are provided for all preprogrammed problems. The check figure for SAMPLE, Requirement 3, is January net income, $2,100. Verify that it agrees with your template.

7. Print the completed template. If you do not have a printer attached to your computer, skip this step for now. To print the template, you will use a preprogrammed print macro. Hold down the ALT key and then press P. When the printing is done, you will note two features of the printout. One, your name is printed exactly the way it was entered on the NAME file (see Lesson 1). Two, the formulas you entered are printed at the bottom of the worksheet. If you have any difficulty executing the print macro, see your instructor.

8. To save your completed template now under the file name SAMPLE3, put the cursor in any cell you wish (cell A1 is suggested). With the

Template Disk in drive B, type /FS, and the computer offers the file name SAMPLE. With Versions 2, 2.01, and 2.2, the computer adds the suffix .WK1. Type the file name **SAMPLE3** and press ENTER. If you had saved the template as SAMPLE, you would have wiped out the original template.

The Template Disk will not hold many extra files; you may need another data disk for your solution templates. To prepare a disk for storing 1-2-3 files, get a blank disk and format it following the instructions on page 14. You should have enough room on the disk to save SAMPLE3, but you should format a blank disk *before* beginning the preprogrammed problems. Remember also that you can use the command **/FEW** (File Erase Worksheet) to delete files from your Template Disk to create extra room for new files.

The next section of each problem is called What-if Analysis. Illustration 18 shows the what-if

What-If Analysis

4) The two options appearing below are being considered to improve the company's monthly net income over the next 5 months. Evaluate the effect on net income for each of these options. Consider each case separately. After evaluating each suggestion, enter the monthly projected net income in the spaces provided below. Assume that both options can be accomplished immediately.

OPTION A: Increase the sales commission rate. This means that sales personnel will receive higher commissions when sales are made. This will increase the selling expense ratio to 70%, but it is also expected to increase the sales growth rate from 2% to 5% per month.

OPTION B: Take some sales people off commissions and put them on straight salary. As a result of this, it is expected that the selling expense ratio will drop to 50%, but general expenses will increase from $1,900 to $2,900 per month. Also, the sales growth rate will drop to 1% per month.

PROJECTED MONTHLY NET INCOME

	JANUARY	FEBRUARY	MARCH	APRIL	MAY
OPTION A	=========	=========	=========	=========	=========
OPTION B	=========	=========	=========	=========	=========

Recommendation:

_____

_____

_____

Illustration 18 Sample Problem Requirement 4

analysis stated in Requirement 4 of the sample problem. It asks you to assess the effect of changes to the original data. The ease with which you will be able to manipulate the problem data and assess the impact on the problem results is an important part of understanding the power and flexibility of electronic spreadsheets. This is the main reason for setting up a separate Data Section for most problems and for structuring the formulas using cell references wherever possible. Explanations of the steps needed to assess the two options presented in Illustration 18 follow.

To explore option A, move the cursor to cell F9, change it to .05, and press ENTER. The template will recalculate, but ignore this since a further change has to be made. Move the cursor now to cell F10, enter .7, and press ENTER. The template should appear as shown in Illustration 19.

Note that if the growth rate and selling expense ratio had not been separately listed in the Data Section, you would have had to change several formulas to analyze option A. Instead, all you had to do was change two numbers!

In the space provided in Illustration 18, write the monthly net incomes. Refer to your printout from Requirement 3 to see if the results are better or worse than the original projection.

To assess option B, move the cursor to cell F9 and change it to .01. Move the cursor to cell F10 and change it to .5. Finally, move the cursor to cell F11 and change it to 2900. Write your answers in the space provided in Illustration 18. The results of option B should appear as shown in Illustration 20 at the top of the next page.

What is your recommendation regarding these two options? Write your answer in the space provided in Illustration 18. Your written answer would be roughly as follows: Given the template results, it seems clear that neither of these two options improves the company's net income projection for the next five months, and both should be rejected.

Your instructor may require you to print the template for each of the what-if scenarios. You will use the print macro (ALT P) to do this.

The final requirement of each problem is in a section entitled GRAPHICS. Not all computers can display graphics. Consult your instructor, and if your computer is incapable of presenting graphical displays, you will not be able to attempt this section.

Requirement 5 of the sample preprogrammed problem is shown in Illustration 21. To begin solving this requirement, you are asked to retrieve

```
F10: (P0) U 0.7                                              READY

       A       B          C        D        E        F        G        H
 6     6 Data Section:
 7     7
 8     8              January sales                      $10,000
 9     9              Sales growth rate                       5%
10    10              Selling expense ratio                  70%
11    11              General expenses                    $1,900
12    12      --------------------------------------------------------------
13    13 Answer Section:
14    14
15    15                         Jan      Feb      Mar      Apr      May
16    16                       -------  -------  -------  -------  -------
17    17 Sales               $10,000  $10,500  $11,025  $11,576  $12,155
18    18
19    19 Selling expenses     $7,000   $7,350   $7,718   $8,103   $8,509
20    20 General expenses      1,900    1,900    1,900    1,900    1,900
21    21                       -------  -------  -------  -------  -------
22    22 Total expenses       $8,900   $9,250   $9,618  $10,003  $10,409
23    23                       -------  -------  -------  -------  -------
24    24 Net income           $1,100   $1,250   $1,408   $1,573   $1,747
25    25                       =======  =======  =======  =======  =======
```

Illustration 19 Screen Display for Option A (lines 6 through 25)

Illustration 20
Screen Display for
Option B (lines 6
through 25)

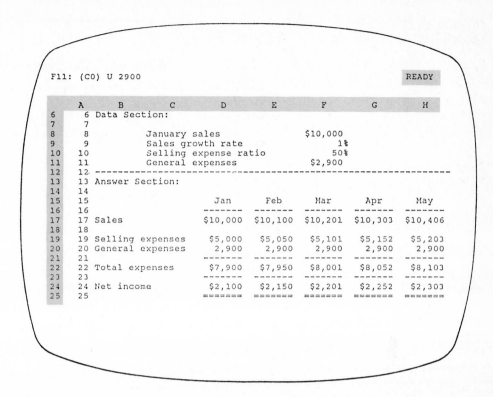

```
F11: (C0) U 2900                                              READY

       A      B       C        D        E        F       G        H
  6    6  Data Section:
  7    7
  8    8           January sales                    $10,000
  9    9           Sales growth rate                     1%
 10   10           Selling expense ratio               50%
 11   11           General expenses                 $2,900
 12   12. ------------------------------------------------------------
 13   13  Answer Section:
 14   14
 15   15                        Jan      Feb      Mar      Apr      May
 16   16                      -------  -------  -------  -------  -------
 17   17  Sales              $10,000  $10,100  $10,201  $10,303  $10,406
 18   18
 19   19  Selling expenses    $5,000   $5,050   $5,101   $5,152   $5,203
 20   20  General expenses     2,900    2,900    2,900    2,900    2,900
 21   21                      -------  -------  -------  -------  -------
 22   22  Total expenses      $7,900   $7,950   $8,001   $8,052   $8,103
 23   23                      -------  -------  -------  -------  -------
 24   24  Net income          $2,100   $2,150   $2,201   $2,252   $2,303
 25   25                      =======  =======  =======  =======  =======
```

Graphics

5) Retrieve the SAMPLE3 template and press the F10 key. A line graph appears on the screen indicating the relationship between sales and total expenses over the 5 month period. The gap between sales and total expenses is net income. Press the ENTER key to return to the net income projections.

A common interest of managers is a company's break-even point. This is the sales volume at which a company's dollar sales are equal to its total expenses. At the break-even point, net income is zero. Only when a company operates above the break-even point will it have profits. Use the graph to find Salyers' break-even point and enter the amount below.

Break-even sales $ _____

Hint: Find a January sales level (cell F8) which causes the two lines to cross. The point at which the two lines cross is the break-even point.

Illustration 21   Problem Requirement 5

Illustration 22
Line Graph

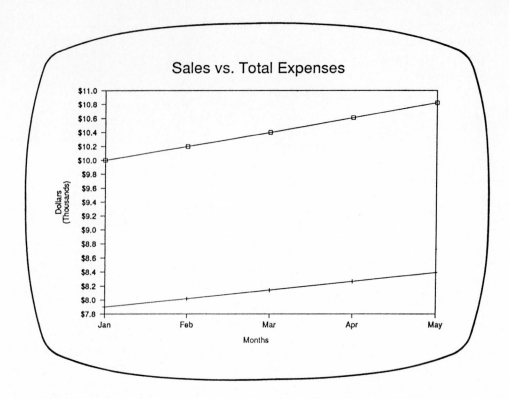

SAMPLE3. This would put the solved template back on the screen with the original data. Since the Data Section for this problem contains only four items, it would be just as easy to leave the current template on the screen and reset the Data Section to the original values. Move the cursor to the Data Section and set cell F9 to .02, cell F10 to .6, and cell F11 to 1900. Then press the F10 key. Immediately the line graph shown in Illustration 22 on page 44 will appear on your screen. (Note: If the graph does not appear, your computer is not configured for graphical display. Press ENTER. You will not be able to attempt this section).

Notice that the sales line is above the total expense line. Thus, with a January sales volume of $10,000, Salyers Enterprises Inc. will earn a positive net income each month because sales are greater than total expenses.

Press ENTER to return to the template and then enter 8000 in cell F8. Press the F10 key again. Notice that the sales and total expenses lines are closer together, but they do not cross. Press ENTER again. Try different values in cell F8, pressing F10 after each attempt, until you get the lines to cross.

A January sales level between $4,400 and $4,750 will result in the sales and total expenses lines crossing on the screen. As you read the graph, you will see that the break-even point is sales of $4,750. At this level of sales, net income is zero. You should now write this answer in the space provided in Illustration 21.

You have now completed the preprogrammed sample problem. The workbook preprogrammed problems begin on page 59.

SAMPLE TEMPLATE TICKLER

The final part of most preprogrammed problems are the ticklers. They are optional sections that differ from the rest of the problem in that their solutions involve altering the template itself. There are three ticklers for the problems: a Template Tickler, a Graphics Tickler, and a Macro Tickler.

The purpose of the Template Ticklers is to demonstrate to you that the workbook templates are not "etched in stone" and that they may be readily adapted to different facts and circumstances. Before completing the sample Template Tickler, you should have worked through Lesson 2 and completed the sample preprogrammed problem (Sample 1).

The Template Tickler for the sample preprogrammed problem is shown in Illustration 23. As you worked through the sample preprogrammed problem (Sample 1), you saved your answer as file SAMPLE3. Load that file now (/FR SAMPLE3).

As a first step toward completing the Template Tickler, you must unprotect the worksheet. Type **/WGPD** (Worksheet Global Protection Disable).

The Template Tickler asks you to insert an additional expense into the model. To add the additional expense to the Data Section, move the cursor to cell C12, type **/WIR** (Worksheet Insert Row), and press ENTER. Then enter the following information:

C12:**Interest expense**
F12:**300**

To format cell F12 for dollars, type **/RFC0** (Range Format Currency 0) and press ENTER twice. Also, type **/RU** (Range Unprotect) and press ENTER.

To alter the Answer Section, use the following steps:

1. Move the cursor to row 22 (old row 21) and insert a new row (/WIR) under General expenses.
2. Renumber the rows in column A by moving the cursor to cell A11, typing /C for Copy, and pressing ENTER. Press the Down Arrow key once, press the Period (.) key, and hold the Down Arrow key down until the cursor is in cell A28. Then press ENTER.
3. Enter **Interest expense** in cell B22.
4. In cell D22, enter the proper formula (**$F12**). The Dollar Sign ($) is needed for Step 6 since the F in F12 is "absolute."
5. To properly format this cell, type **/RF,0** and press ENTER twice.
6. Copy the formula in cell D22 to cells E22 through H22.

TEMPLATE TICKLER

Retrieve the SAMPLE3 template. Late in December, Salyers had to obtain a bank loan to pay some business debts. The interest expense for this loan will amount to $300 per month. Alter the template to include Interest Expense as an additional input item in the Data Section and also include the interest as an additional expense in the Answer Section (put it right under General Expenses).

Save the completed template as SAMPLET. Print the modified worksheet when done.

Illustration 23 Sample Problem Template Tickler

7. Modify the total expenses formula for January using either of the following formulas:

D24:+D20+D21+D22 or @SUM(D20.D22)

8. Copy the total expense formula for January to the other cells in that row.

When you are done, the template should appear as shown in Illustration 24.

To reprotect your altered worksheet, press /WGPE.

The print macro will not work with the Template Tickler. To print the modified template, enter /PPR and type **A1.H28** to indicate the range. Then press ENTER. Next, press **A** and then **G** to begin printing. When the printing is complete, press **P** to eject the page and then **Q** to quit. Save your modified masterpiece using the file name SAMPLET (/FS SAMPLET).

As a reminder, for templates over 60 rows deep, you may want to eliminate the automatic page breaks. To accomplish this, type **/PPOOUQ** (Print Printer Options Other Unformatted Quit) before pressing **Go**. This unformatted printing style was discussed in Lesson 1. Also, remember to print extra-wide templates in compressed mode (see Lesson 1 for details).

```
SAMPLE                Student Name    =>
                      Section Number  =>
     ------------------------------------------------------------------
     A      B       C       D       E       F       G       H
     ------------------------------------------------------------------
   6 Data Section:
   7
   8              January sales           $10,000
   9              Sales growth rate              2%
  10              Selling expense ratio         60%
  11              General expenses         $1,900
  12              Interest expense          $300
  13       ------------------------------------------------------------
  14 Answer Section:
  15
  16                      Jan     Feb     Mar     Apr     May
  17                    ------- ------- ------- ------- -------
  18 Sales            $10,000 $10,200 $10,404 $10,612 $10,824
  19
  20 Selling expenses  $6,000  $6,120  $6,242  $6,367  $6,495
  21 General expenses   1,900   1,900   1,900   1,900   1,900
  22 Interest expense     300     300     300     300     300
  23                    ------- ------- ------- ------- -------
  24 Total expenses    $8,200  $8,320  $8,442  $8,567  $8,695
  25                    ------- ------- ------- ------- -------
  26 Net income        $1,800  $1,880  $1,962  $2,045  $2,130
  27                    ======= ======= ======= ======= =======
  28       ------------------------------------------------------------
```

Illustration 24 Completed Template for Template Tickler

SAMPLE 3

SAMPLE GRAPHICS TICKLER

The purpose of the Graphics Ticklers is to introduce the various graphing options available in the Lotus 1-2-3 program. Before completing the sample Graphics Tickler, you should complete Lesson 3, which describes how graphs are created and printed.

The Graphics Tickler for the sample preprogrammed problem is shown in Illustration 25 below. To complete the tickler, load the SAMPLE3 file from your disk and do the following:

1. After SAMPLE3 is retrieved, press the F10 key. The graph shown on the screen is the line graph you dealt with when you completed Sample 1. See the line graph shown in Illustration 22 on page 44. This is called the "current" graph. Press ENTER to get back to the READY mode.

2. Your first step is to complete the graph data table. Type **/WGPD** to disable the worksheet protection.

3. Enter formulas in the following cells:
    D39: **+H19**
    D40: **+H20**
    D41: **+H24**

4. Type **/WGPE** to reprotect the worksheet.

5. Press **/G** for Graph, **N** for Name, **C** for Create, enter the name **ORIG**, and press ENTER. This saves the current graph in memory for later recall.

6. Type **R** for Reset and **G** for Graph. This removes the line graph from current memory and allows you to start over with a new graph. The line graph can still be recalled using the Graph Name Use command.

7. Press **T** for Type and **P** for Pie.

8. Press **X** for X-axis, enter the range **B39.B41**, and press ENTER.

9. Press **A** for A-range, enter the range **D39.D41**, and press ENTER.

10. Press **O** for Options, **T** for Titles, **F** for First, enter **Distribution of May Sales Revenue**, and press ENTER.

11. Press **Q** to Quit and **V** to View. When done viewing, press ENTER.

12. Press **S** to Save, type the graph file name **SAMPLEG**, and press ENTER. The pie graph has now been saved as a PIC file and can be printed on the printer.

13. Press **Q** to Quit, type **/FS SAMPLE3** to Save, press ENTER, and then press **R** to Replace the revised template.

14. To print the graph, you will need the Lotus 1-2-3 PrintGraph Disk. Press **/QY** to quit 1-2-3. The screen you now see is the 1-2-3 Access System Menu.

15. Type **P** to select PrintGraph and insert the PrintGraph Disk when requested.

GRAPHICS TICKLER

Retrieve the SAMPLE3 template. Type /Graph, Name, Create, ORIG, and press ENTER. Then press Reset and Graph. Prepare a pie graph which shows the proportionate amount of May sales spent for selling expenses, general expenses, and the amount left over for net income. Complete the graphics data table in rows 36-41 and use it as a basis for preparing the graph. Use **B39.H41** as the X-axis and **D39.D41** as the A-range. Save the graph as a PIC file called SAMPLEG. Print the graph.

Illustration 25 Sample Problem Graphics Tickler

16. Press **S** for Select (**I** for Image-Select in Versions 2, 2.01, and 2.2), mark SAMPLEG as the file to be printed, and press ENTER.
17. Turn your printer on and press **G** for Go.
18. When the graph is printed, press **P** to eject the page. Your graph should appear as shown in Illustration 26.

19. To return to Lotus 1-2-3, press **Q** to Quit the PrintGraph program (press **EY** in Versions 2, 2.01, and 2.2) and then remove the PrintGraph Disk. Reinsert the Lotus 1-2-3 System Disk and press ENTER. (For Versions 2, 2.01, and 2.2, type **LOTUS** if the A> prompt appears.)

Distribution of May Sales Revenue

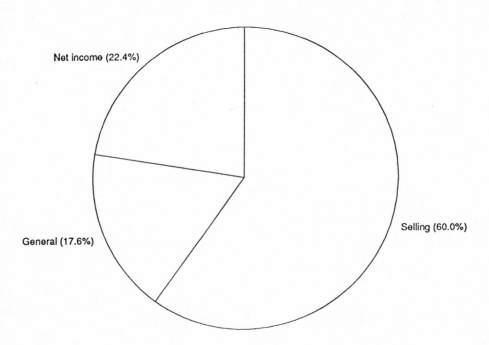

Net income (22.4%)

General (17.6%)

Selling (60.0%)

Illustration 26 Printout of Graphics Tickler

SAMPLE 4
SAMPLE MACRO TICKLER

The purpose of the Macro Ticklers is to acquaint you with the programming feature of Lotus 1-2-3. Before completing the sample Macro Tickler, you should complete Lesson 4, which introduces the basic procedures for creating macros.

The Macro Tickler for the sample pre-programmed problem is stated in Illustration 27. The tickler asks you to develop a macro that will add a heading to the net income projection completed in the file SAMPLE3 and print out the template after adding the heading.

Load the file SAMPLE3 now. The macro should not interfere physically or visually with the worksheet itself. For this example, the macro will begin in cell B30.

Type /WGPD to unprotect the worksheet. The macro is shown in bold below. The explanations below each line of the macro explain what each step of the macro will accomplish.

B30:{GOTO}A14~

The cursor moves to the point where rows will be inserted.

B31:'/WIR{DOWN}{DOWN}~

The range of rows to be added is specified. The apostrophe will not show up on the screen in cell B31.

B32:{GOTO}A13~/C~A14.A29~

The row numbers are revised.

B33:{GOTO}D14~' Salyers Enterprises Inc.~

The company name will appear on the first line of the heading. Be careful to insert two spaces after the apostrophe.

B34:{DOWN}' Net Income Projection~

The statement title will appear on the second line of the heading. Insert three spaces after the apostrophe.

B35:{DOWN}' For January-May, 19XX~

The dates covered by the statement will appear on the third line of the heading. Insert three spaces after the apostrophe.

B36:'/PPRA1.H29~AGQ{HOME}

The range A1 to H29 will be printed, and the cursor will be returned to cell A1. Again, the apostrophe will not show up on the screen in cell B36.

After you have entered the macro, you must create a named range for the macro. To create a range name, move the cursor to cell B30 and type /RNC. You will be asked to specify a name. All the macros must begin with a Backslash (\). You should type \R as the name for the range and press ENTER to accept B30 as the named range. Only the top cell in a macro needs to be in the range name.

In order to remember the name you have given the macro, you should move the cursor to cell A30 and type '\R.

MACRO TICKLER

Retrieve the SAMPLE3 template. Prepare a macro named /R which will add a heading to the net income projection and which will print the revised template. The heading should include the company name, a title for the statement, and appropriate dates.

Illustration 27   Sample Problem for Macro Tickler

Since the execution of this macro will alter your template, it would be best to save the macro (and your template!) before trying the macro. Type /FS and press ENTER to save your macro and completed template as SAMPLE3. Press **R** to Replace the original.

You are now ready to execute the macro. With the cursor in any cell, hold down the ALT key and press **R**. As you observe the screen, you will see the steps of the macro performed. When the macro is completed, 1-2-3 will return to the READY mode.

If your macro does not work on the first try, it will need to be debugged. Press ESC to get back to the READY mode and then review the template to see how far the macro proceeded before crashing. Then, retrieve SAMPLE3 again and, if necessary, personally execute your macro one keystroke at a time and watch what happens on the screen. You may use the STEP mode discussed in Lesson 4 to accomplish this. When you uncover your error, use the F2 key to edit the erroneous part of your macro. Before trying to execute your revision, make sure that you save it again as SAMPLE3.

When you get the macro to work correctly, reprotect your worksheet with the /WGPE command. Save your completed worksheet as SAMPLE3 again. Your printout should appear as shown in Illustration 28 .

```
SAMPLE                     Student Name    =>
                           Section Number  =>
    ------------------------------------------------------------------------
    A       B       C       D       E       F       G       H
    ------------------------------------------------------------------------
     6 Data Section:
     7
     8              January sales            $10,000
     9              Sales growth rate             2%
    10              Selling expense ratio        60%
    11              General expenses          $1,900
    12 --------------------------------------------------------------------
    13 Answer Section:
    14                      Salyers Enterprises Inc.
    15                      Net Income Projection
    16                      For January-May, 19XX
    17
    18                      Jan     Feb     Mar     Apr     May
    19                      ------- ------- ------- ------- -------
    20 Sales               $10,000 $10,200 $10,404 $10,612 $10,824
    21
    22 Selling expenses     $6,000  $6,120  $6,242  $6,367  $6,495
    23 General expenses      1,900   1,900   1,900   1,900   1,900
    24                      ------- ------- ------- ------- -------
    25 Total expenses       $7,900  $8,020  $8,142  $8,267  $8,395
    26                      ------- ------- ------- ------- -------
    27 Net income           $2,100  $2,180  $2,262  $2,345  $2,430
    28                      ======= ======= ======= ======= =======
    29 --------------------------------------------------------------------
```

Illustration 28 Completed Printout for Macro Tickler

SAMPLE 5

SAMPLE MODEL-BUILDING PROBLEM

Model-building problems require you to design spreadsheet models from start to finish. Nothing has been preprogrammed for you. Basic suggestions for developing spreadsheet models are contained in Lesson 5.

The model-building problems contain two sets of input and an optional graphics component. The first set of input is for you to use in designing your model. The second set will be used by your instructor to test your model to see if it performs the proper computations. Your instructor should not have to change anything in your model except the input data. Thus, you must be very careful in structuring your model.

You have been provided with both sets of data so that you can:

a. specifically identify which variables in the problem will change and which ones won't.
b. double check your model to see that it functions properly with different inputs.

The purpose of this sample problem is to show you how to approach the model-building problems in this workbook. To accomplish this, we will work through the sample model-building problem that appears in Illustration 29. Read the problem now.

TRIAL BALANCE

The general ledger of Upton Services shows the following account balances at May 31:

Cash	$ 1,665.38
Accounts receivable	614.00
Accounts payable	610.64
Lindsay Upton, capital	8,000.00
Lindsay Upton, drawing	7,500.00
Revenue	46,590.80
Rent expense	5,000.00
Salary expense	32,950.00
Supplies expense	7,472.06

Lindsay Upton has asked you to develop a template (file name TB) that will be a trial balance. Use the data above as input for your model. Your answer should include all appropriate titles and headings above the columns.

Print the template when done and also print the cell contents. (Check figure: Trial balance total, $55,201.44)

To test your model, use the following balances at June 30:

Cash	$ 1,484.20
Accounts receivable	415.51
Accounts payable	2,144.48
Lindsay Upton, capital	8,000.00
Lindsay Upton, drawing	9,000.00
Revenue	57,371.70
Rent expense	6,000.00
Salary expense	41,556.00
Supplies expense	9,060.47

Print the template when done. (Check figure: Trial balance total, $67,516.18)

Graphics (optional)

Prepare a bar graph which compares the total expenses incurred in May with the total incurred in June. Print the graph when done.

Illustration 29 Sample Model-Building Statement

Before turning on the computer, some attempt should be made to lay out the structure of your answer on paper. As mentioned in Lesson 5, careful planning on paper can eliminate hours of wasted time on the computer. Fortunately, 1-2-3 is forgiving enough that most refinements to a preliminary plan can be done "on the fly" while working at the computer.

This model-building problem requires you to develop a spreadsheet model that is a trial balance. Assuming you have had beginning accounting, you can probably visualize the answer format rather quickly. A trial balance is a schedule which lists all accounts and their balances. When done, the total of the accounts with debit balances should equal the total of the accounts with credit balances. You might sketch out the following on paper to get you started:

Account Name	Debit	Credit
Cash	$1,665.38	
A/R	614.00	
Ppd. Ins.	1,200.00	
A/P		$ 610.64

Totals	$ SUM	$ SUM
	=======	=======

This is roughly what the answer will look like. The next major question to resolve is whether or not to use a Data Section for all of the changeable input values required to complete the model. A Data Section should always be given strong consideration since it helps highlight the numerical assumptions of the model and it facilitates performing what-if analysis.

This decision relies on your judgment. As mentioned in Lesson 5, a "direct-entry" model is more appropriate than one using a Data Section in those cases where formulas do not have to be revised to accommodate the introduction of new data. In this trial balance model, there are only two formulas (the sums at the bottom of each column), and they do not need to be rewritten as new data (account balances) is entered. Therefore, a "direct-entry" model is better for this particular model.

Now let's begin work on the computer. Load 1-2-3 and insert a disk in drive B on which you can save your work. This could be your Template Disk if you still have room on it, or some other formatted disk. (See Lesson 1 for instructions on formatting and preparing a new disk.)

After 1-2-3 is loaded, enter your name and section number in cell A1. Enter the file name given to you in the problem in cell A2. The file name given for this problem is TB.

Now we begin building the model. You will learn very quickly that making and correcting mistakes is a frequent occurrence when building models. Thus, in the instructions that follow, you will be purposely led into making a couple mistakes and then shown how to correct them. With Version 2.2 the Undo feature (ALT F4) can be very helpful for this purpose.

Based on your initial plan, it appears that column B can be used for entering account names, and columns F and G can be used to record the debit and credit balances. So, enter the following labels:

> B5:^Account Name
> F5:^Debit
> G5:^Credit

Now let's underline the headings.

> B6:\─ then copy to cells C6.D6
> F6:'──────── then copy to cell G6

The standard column width is nine characters. The entries in cells F6 and G6 put eight dashes in each. This leaves the ninth character blank and creates a visual separation between the columns.

Move the cursor to column B and type the following account names:

> B7:Cash
> B8:Accounts receivable
> B9:Accounts payable
> B10:Lindsay Upton, capital
> B11:Lindsay Upton, drawing
> B12:Revenue
> B13:Rent expense
> B14:Salary expense
> B15:Supplies expense
>
> B17:Totals

Do not enter anything in cell B16.

To enter the amounts, move to cell F7. In beginning accounting, you learned that accounts that normally have debit balances are assets, drawing, and expense accounts. Those that normally have credit balances are liabilities, equity, and revenues. Using this knowledge, enter the listed values in the appropriate columns as follows:

> F7:1665.38
> F8:614
> G9:610.64

G10:**8000**
G12:**46590.8**
F11:**7500**
F13:**5000**
F14:**32950**
F15:**7472.06**

Enter underlines in columns F and G.

F16:**'———— then copy to cell G16**

Enter the summation formulas in columns F and G. Recall that @SUM is a special function command. @SUM and many other special function commands are discussed in Appendix C.

F17:**@SUM(F7.F15)** then copy to cell G17

The totals found in cells F17 and G17 should be equal. If they aren't, find your mistake before proceeding. In addition, check figures are provided for all model-building problems. The check figure for the model is that the trial balance total for May is $55,201.44. Verify that it agrees with your template.

Enter double underlines (equal signs) under the totals.

F18:**'======== then copy to cell G18**

At this point, your template should appear as in Illustration 30 below.

As mentioned in Lesson 5, it is always a good idea to save your work periodically so that an accidental hardware failure does not destroy your efforts. Let's do this now. With your template disk in drive B, type **/FS TB**, and press ENTER.

Now let's clean up the value formats in columns F and G. We will put Dollar Signs ($) at the top and bottom of the columns using the **Currency** format, and everything else will be put in the **Comma** format. Because the problem data is provided in dollars and cents, we will use two decimal places in all cells in your answer.

Since the cursor is at the bottom of the worksheet, let's begin there. Move the cursor to cell F17 and type **/RFC** (Range Format Currency). Press ENTER to accept 2 as the number of decimals. Press the Right Arrow key once and then press ENTER to complete the range (cells F17 and G17).

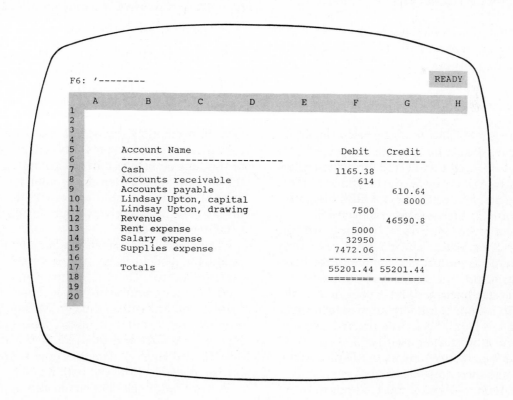

Illustration 30 Trial Balance for May

Oops! We've got our first problem. With a comma and a dollar sign added to the cells, there are too many characters for the cells to hold. So, let's expand the column width. Type **/WCS** (Worksheet Column-width Set). We could type **10** and press ENTER now to see if that width works, but a better way to try 10 is to simply press the Right Arrow key once. Try that now. Automatically the column width expands by one, but it is still not wide enough for the value to reappear.

Press the Right Arrow key once again to expand the column width to 11. Now the number reappears. If this worksheet is to be designed for reuse each month, we should consider that a column width of 11 may not be enough because our totals will most certainly be over $99,999.99 by year end. To accommodate a number this large, we need to go one more character. Press the Right Arrow key once more, then press ENTER. Set column G to 12 characters also.

Now notice another problem on the worksheet. The underlines and double underlines are too short. This is easy to correct.

1. Move the cursor to cell F6.
2. Press the **F2** key (Edit key).
3. Type three dashes and press ENTER.
4. Repeat this in cells G6, F16, and G16. In cells F18 and G18, use double underlines. Note: The Copy command could also be used to copy the revised contents of cell F6 to cells G6, F16, and G16.

Let's get back to formatting the cells now. Move the cursor to cell F15 and type **/RF,** (don't forget the comma). Press ENTER to accept two decimals. Now paint the area to be formatted by pressing the Up Arrow key seven times (until it reaches cell F8) and the Right Arrow key once. Then press ENTER. Move the cursor to cell F7. Type **/RFC** and press ENTER twice. Do the same thing for cell G9.

What we need now is a heading for the worksheet. Here again, you must use your judgment. It would seem that at a minimum the heading should include the name of the company, the name of the statement, and the date or time period involved. To include this information attractively at the top of the worksheet, let's insert three new rows. Move the cursor to row 4, type **/WIR** (Worksheet Insert Row), press the Down Arrow key twice, and then press ENTER.

Where columns D and E meet is approximately half way across the screen. To center the headings, move the cursor to cell D4, press the Space Bar twice, type **Upton Services**, and press ENTER. Move the cursor to cell D5, press the Space Bar three times, type **Trial Balance**, and press ENTER. Move the cursor to cell D6, press the Space Bar once, type **For the Month of**, and press ENTER. Move the cursor to cell F6, type **May**, and press ENTER. The month name has been placed in a separate cell so that it can be easily changed throughout the year without having to retype "For the Month of" over and over.

Finally, move the cursor to cell B7, type **\-**, and press ENTER. Then copy this to the range C7.G7. When done, your model should appear as shown in Illustration 31 on the next page.

The last step in building the model is to protect it. Everything that will remain the same month after month should be protected. Items that will change should be left unprotected. Review the test data provided in the problem statement in Illustration 29. After reviewing the test data, it is apparent that the account balances will (or could) change each month, as will the date.

To begin the protection process, type **/WGPE** (Worksheet Global Protection Enable). Then move the cursor to cell F6, type **/RU** (Range Unprotect), and press ENTER. Next move the cursor to cell F10, type **/RU** again, use the arrow keys to paint in the range to be unprotected (F10 to G18), and then press ENTER.

It is now time to save your model again to insure that your work will not be lost. Type **/FS**, press ENTER to accept TB as the file name, and type **R** to replace the previously saved file.

Let's test your model now using the test data from Illustration 29 on page 51. Move the cursor to cell F6, type **June**, and press ENTER. Next, enter all of the June 30 balances in the appropriate cells of the trial balance. When done, your totals should balance, and they should agree with the check figure for June 30. The check figure for the June trial balance is $67,516.18.

When the test data answer agrees with the check figure, the model can be printed for submission to your instructor. There is no print macro for the model-building problems. You will have to use the Print commands discussed in Lesson 1. For example, to print your trial balance model you would type **/PPRA1.G21** and press ENTER. Then type **A** and **G**, and then **Q**. Try this now if you have a printer available. Print out both months.

A printout of cell contents is also required. See Lesson 1 for instructions.

Illustration 31
Completed Trial Balance
Model (lines 1 through 20)

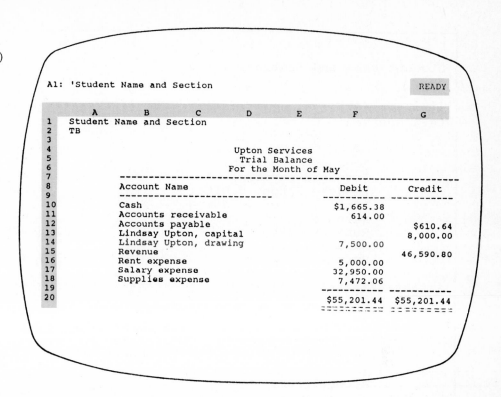

```
A1:  'Student Name and Section                                    READY

        A         B         C         D         E         F         G
1   Student Name and Section
2   TB
3
4                                    Upton Services
5                                    Trial Balance
6                                    For the Month of May
7   -------------------------------------------------------------------
8   Account Name                                        Debit       Credit
9   --------------------------                       -----------  -----------
10  Cash                                             $1,665.38
11  Accounts receivable                                 614.00
12  Accounts payable                                                 $610.64
13  Lindsay Upton, capital                                          8,000.00
14  Lindsay Upton, drawing                            7,500.00
15  Revenue                                                        46,590.80
16  Rent expense                                      5,000.00
17  Salary expense                                   32,950.00
18  Supplies expense                                  7,472.06
19                                                   -----------  -----------
20                                                  $55,201.44   $55,201.44
                                                   ===========  ===========
```

Before we leave this lesson, what might this model have looked like if a Data Section had been used? Illustration 32 on the next page presents a printout of one possibility. The cells in the range F7 to F15 are unprotected as is cell F22. All cells in columns F and G of the Answer Section contain formulas which reference the appropriate cells in the Data Section. The formula in cell F26 is +F7, the formula in cell F27 is +F8, and so forth. This would be a good model design for a bookkeeper who had difficulty keeping debits and credits straight!

The optional graphics section calls for the creation of a bar graph based on data found in both months. Since the graphics data cannot be placed easily into ranges on the current template, a graphics data table should be prepared at the bottom of the worksheet area. Use the template with the June data entered. The table should not interfere (physically or visually) with the worksheet itself. Let's place it beginning in row 30 using the following steps:

1. Type **/WGPD** to disable the worksheet protection.
2. Use the following table to enter the labels, values, and formulas in the cells specified (the row and column labels are provided for reference only and should not be keyed).

	B	D	E
30	Graphics Data	May	June
31	Rent	5000	+F16 (or 6000)
32	Salary	32950	+F17 (or 41556)
33	Supplies	7472.06	+F18 (or 9060.47)

3. Reprotect the worksheet by typing **/WGPE**.
4. Type **/G** for Graph, **T** for Type, and **B** for Bar.
5. Type **X** for X-axis, enter the range **B31.B33**, and press ENTER.
6. Type **A** for A-range, enter the range **D31.D33**, and press ENTER.
7. Type **B** for B-range, enter the range **E31.E33**, and press ENTER.
8. Type **O** for Options, **T** for Titles, **F** for First, enter **Expenses - Upton Services**, and press ENTER.
9. Type **L** for Legend, **A** for A-range, enter **May**, and press ENTER.
10. Type **L** for Legend, **B** for B-range, enter **June**, and press ENTER.

```
Student Name and Section
TB

****************************************************************
Data Section:

        Cash                                    $1,665.38
        Accounts receivable                        614.00
        Accounts payable                           610.64
        Lindsay Upton, capital                   8,000.00
        Lindsay Upton, drawing                   7,500.00
        Revenue                                 46,590.80
        Rent expense                             5,000.00
        Salary expense                          32,950.00
        Supplies expense                         7,472.06


****************************************************************
Answer Section:

                        Upton Services
                        Trial Balance
                     For the Month of May
        ------------------------------------------------------
        Account Name                    Debit        Credit
        ------------------------------ ----------- -----------
        Cash                            $1,665.38
        Accounts receivable                614.00
        Accounts payable                              $610.64
        Lindsay Upton, capital                       8,000.00
        Lindsay Upton, drawing           7,500.00
        Revenue                                     46,590.80
        Rent expense                     5,000.00
        Salary expense                  32,950.00
        Supplies expense                 7,472.06
                                       ----------- -----------
                                       $55,201.44  $55,201.44
                                       =========== ===========

****************************************************************
```

Illustration 32   Completed Trial Balance Model With Data Section

11. Type **S** for Scale, **Y** for Y-axis, **F** for Format, **C** for Currency, **0** for zero decimal places, and press ENTER.
12. Press **Q** to Quit twice and **V** to View. Press ENTER when done viewing.
13. Type **S** for Save, enter **TBG** as the graph file name, and press ENTER. The graph has now been saved as a picture file.
14. Press **Q** to Quit, type **/FS TB**, and press ENTER to save the template file itself. Press **R** to Replace.
15. To print the graph you will need the Lotus 1-2-3 PrintGraph Disk. Press **/QY** to quit 1-2-3. The

screen you now see is the Lotus 1-2-3 Access System Menu.
16. Type **P** to select PrintGraph and insert the PrintGraph Disk when requested.
17. Press **S** for Select (**I** for Image-Select in Versions 2, 2.01, and 2.2) and select TBG as the file to be printed.
18. Turn your printer on and press **G** for Go.
19. When the graph is printed, press **P** to eject the page. Your graph should appear as shown in Illustration 33.
20. To return to Lotus 1-2-3, press **Q** to Quit the PrintGraph program (press **EY** in Versions 2,

56

2.01, and 2.2) and then remove the PrintGraph Disk. Reinsert the Lotus 1-2-3 System Disk and press ENTER. (For Versions 2, 2.01 and 2.2, type **LOTUS** if the A> prompt appears.)

The workbook model-building problems begin on page 181.

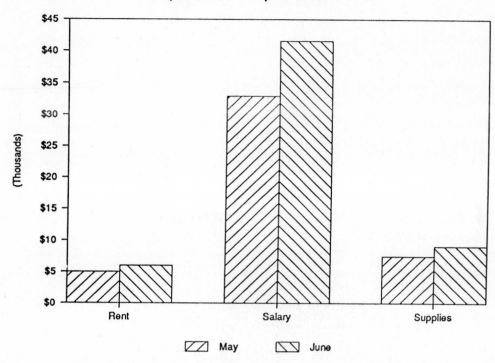

Illustration 33 Printout of Bar Graph

P1 BUSINESS TRANSACTIONS (TRANSACT)

On September 1 of the current year, Jill Squires opened Squires Professional Resume Service. The sole proprietorship had the following transactions during September.

a. Opened a business checking account and made a deposit, $2,000.
b. Paid rent for September for office space and equipment, $450.
c. Purchased office supplies (stamps, pens, etc.) on account, $406.
d. Received cash for services rendered, $825.
e. Paid creditor for office supplies purchased on account, $200.
f. Purchased office supplies for cash, $86.
g. Billed clients for consultations performed on account, $900.
h. Paid utility bill of $90.
i. Paid the secretary's salary of $650.
j. Cash was withdrawn for owner's personal use, $200.
k. Received cash from clients previously billed, $700.
l. Returned $50 of office supplies purchased in Transaction _f_ above. Received a full refund.

Required

1) Review the template called TRANSACT. You have been asked to complete the template by recording these transactions.

2) There are five formulas requested to complete the template. Using the spaces provided below, write the formulas required to complete the template.

FORMULA1 _____   FORMULA4 _____

FORMULA2 _____   FORMULA5 _____

FORMULA3 _____

3) Load the spreadsheet program and then load the template TRANSACT. Enter the formulas in the appropriate cells on the template. Then enter the increases and decreases resulting from each transaction on the template. For example, the first transaction increases the cash account by $2,000 and also increases the capital account by $2,000. This transaction has already been recorded on the template. The template will automatically total each column as values are entered in that column. When you are finished, check line 30 to make sure that total assets equal total liabilities and equity.

4) It has been determined that the cost of the supplies used during the month was $175. Record the increase or decrease in the appropriate columns on the template. This is Transaction _m_ above. Save the completed template as TRANSAC4. Press ALT P to print the worksheet when done. _Check figure: Ending cash balance (cell C25), $1,899_

5) How does Transaction _m_ differ from Transactions _a_ through _l_? In other words, why is it treated as a special item?

_____

_____

_____

_____

6) Use the forms below to prepare an income statement, statement of owner's equity, and balance sheet in good form for Squires Professional Resume Service for the month of September.

What-If Analysis

7) Jill invested $2,000 initially in the business. Could she have invested less? How little could she have invested initially and never have her cash balance go below zero? To help answer this question, move the cursor to column K and analyze the information provided. Then enter different amounts in cell C11 to help determine an answer. When you have determined an answer, use ALT Q to print the worksheet. Explain how you derived your answer below.

_____

_____

_____

_____

_____

_____

_____

_____

_____

_____

Graphics

8) Retrieve the TRANSAC4 template. Press the F10 key. A pie graph appears on the screen indicating the percentage of each asset in relation to total assets. Jill does not want her cash balance to exceed 65% of her total assets. How much does she have to withdraw to reduce her cash percentage to 65%? To find out, enter different (negative) values in cell C23, pressing the ENTER and F10 keys after each entry. When you find the withdrawal amount that decreases the cash percentage to 65%, enter that amount in the space provided below.

Withdrawal needed $_____

TEMPLATE TICKLER

Retrieve the TRANSAC4 template. Two additional transactions occurred in September which need to be recorded on the template.

n. Billed customers for additional services rendered on account, $500.
o. Paid creditor for office supplies purchased on account, $50.

Expand the template to include these transactions. Do not revise column K.

Hint: Remove the worksheet protection. Move the cursor to row 24 and insert two new rows. In column B, label the new rows as n and o. Update the row numbers in column A. Revise the summation formulas. Record the transactions. Save the template as TRANSTT. Print the template (columns A through I) when done.

GRAPHICS TICKLER

Retrieve the TRANSAC4 template. Print the graph which appears when you press the F10 key. To create the PIC file needed for printing, save the graph as TRANSG.

MACRO TICKLER

Retrieve the TRANSAC4 template. Create a macro named \R to print columns B through I and rows 6 through 31 only.

```
TRANSACT                  Student Name    =
                          Section Number  =
-----------------------------------------------------------------------------
 A     B       C          D          E       F      G      H      I
-----------------------------------------------------------------------------
 6                      Assets               = Liabilities + Equity
 7             ----------------------------   ------------   ---------
 8                      Accts.     Office     Accts.                  Squires,
 9             Cash    + Rec.    + Supp.    = Payable     + Capital
10             ------    ------     ------     --------       --------
11    a)       $2,000       $0         $0            $0          $2,000
12    b)
13    c)
14    d)
15    e)
16    f)
17    g)
18    h)
19    i)
20    j)
21    k)
22    l)
23    m)
24             --------  --------  --------   --------       --------
25             FORMULA1 FORMULA2 FORMULA3     FORMULA4        FORMULA5
26             ======== ======== ========     ========       ========
27
28
29             Total                          Total liabilities
30             assets =        $0             and equity =          $0
31    -----------------------------------------------------------------------
```

The trial balance of Bonnie Cleaners at August 31, 19X0, the end of the current fiscal year, is below:

Bonnie Cleaners
Trial Balance
August 31, 19X0

Cash	$ 4,400	
Cleaning Supplies	7,300	
Prepaid Insurance	1,800	
Equipment	68,700	
Accumulated Depreciation		$ 24,700
Accounts Payable		2,480
R. MacKay, Capital		45,200
R. MacKay, Drawing	18,000	
Revenue		51,740
Rent Expense	9,500	
Wages Expense	13,240	
Utilities Expense	710	
Miscellaneous Expense	470	
	$124,120	$124,120
	======	======

Information for the adjusting entries is as follows:

a. Cleaning supplies on hand on August 31, 19X0, $6,250
b. Insurance premiums expired during the year, $600
c. Depreciation on equipment during the year, $7,200
d. Wages accrued but not paid at August 31, 19X0, $610

Required

1) As the accountant for Bonnie Cleaners, you have been asked to prepare financial statements for the year. A template called WSHEET has been provided to assist you in this assignment. As you review this template, it should be noted that columns J and K will automatically change when you enter values in columns G or I.

2) There are eight formulas requested to complete the template. Using the spaces provided below, write the formulas required to complete the template.

FORMULA1 _____   FORMULA5 _____

FORMULA2 _____   FORMULA6 _____

FORMULA3 _____   FORMULA7 _____

FORMULA4 _____   FORMULA8 _____

3) Load the spreadsheet program and then load the template WSHEET. Enter the formulas in the appropriate cells on the template. Then enter the adjusting amounts in columns G and I. Also, in column F or H, insert the letter corresponding to the adjusting entry (a - d). Columns A through C are "frozen" on the screen to assist you in completing Requirement 4.

4) Complete the income statement and balance sheet by entering the appropriate formulas in columns L, M, N, and O. (Do not use the copy command to accomplish this. Enter formulas referencing the appropriate cells in columns J or K.) Net income will be automatically calculated for the income statement and balance sheet. Check to be sure that these numbers are the same. Save the completed template as WSHEET4. If you have an IBM or Epson printer, press ALT C to print the template in compressed mode. If not, press ALT P and the worksheet will automatically print in two sections. *Check figure: Net income (cell L36), $18,360*

What-If Analysis

5) Suppose you discover that an assistant in your department had misunderstood your instructions and had provided you with wrong information on two of the adjusting entries. Cleaning supplies consumed during the year should have been $6,250, and insurance premiums unexpired at year-end were $600. Make the corrections on your worksheet and reprint it. Save the corrected file as WSHEET5.

6) Use the forms below to prepare an income statement, a capital statement, and a balance sheet, using the corrected worksheet (WSHEET5). Assume that no additional owner investments were made during the year.

Graphics

7) Retrieve WSHEET5 and press the F10 key. On the screen, a pie chart shows the percentage compositions of the total expenses of Bonnie Cleaners. Enter the percentages below. Compare the percentages of Bonnie Cleaners with the national statistics provided. Comment on the differences noted. Why might depreciation, utilities, and rent be so far off from the national percentages?

	National Averages	Bonnie Cleaners
Wages	33.0%	
Rent	12.3	
Depreciation	23.8	
Supplies	17.5	
Insurance	4.7	
Utilities	7.7	
Misc.	1.0	_____
	100.0%	
	=====	=====

TEMPLATE TICKLER

Include the income statement on the WSHEET5 template. Remove the freeze on columns A through C by typing **/WTC**. Beginning on line 41 of the template, set up the outline of the income statement (headings, etc.) that was required to be handwritten in Requirement 6 of the problem. Enter formulas in the outline to reference the appropriate income statement cells in the worksheet. Use proper formats for all value cells. Save the template as WSHEETT. Print the income statement (not the whole worksheet) when done.

GRAPHICS TICKLER

Retrieve WSHEET5. Remove the freeze on columns A through C by typing **/WTC**. Type /Graph, Name, Create, **ORIG**, and press ENTER. Then press Reset and Graph. Create a bar graph showing the dollar total of each of the expenses of Bonnie Cleaners. Use B71.B77 as the X-axis (shorten the titles) and C71.C77 as the A-range. Save the graph as a PIC file called WSHEETG. Save the template again as WSHEET5. Print the graph.

MACRO TICKLER

Retrieve the WSHEET5. Create a macro named **\R** to print the worksheet without columns D through K showing.

WSHEET

Student Name =>
Section Number =>

Bonnie Cleaners
Work Sheet
For Year Ended August 31, 19X0

Spreadsheet columns: A B C D E F G H I J K L M N O

Row	Account Title	Trial Balance Dr.	Trial Balance Cr.	Adjustments Dr.	Adjustments Cr.	Adj. T/Balance Dr.	Adj. T/Balance Cr.	Income Statement Dr.	Income Statement Cr.	Balance Sheet Dr.	Balance Sheet Cr.
13	Cash	4,400				4,400	0				
14	Cleaning supplies	7,300				7,300	0				
15	Prepaid insurance	1,800				1,800	0				
16	Equipment	68,700				68,700	0				
17	Accumulated depr.		24,700			0	24,700				
18	Accounts payable		2,480			0	2,480				
19	R. MacKay, capital		45,200			0	45,200				
20	R. MacKay, drawing	18,000				18,000	0				
21	Revenue		51,740			0	51,740				
22	Rent expense	9,500				9,500	0				
23	Wages expense	13,240				13,240	0				
24	Utilities expense	710				710	0				
25	Misc. expense	470				470	0				
27		124,120	124,120								
29	Supplies expense					0	0				
30	Insurance expense					0	0				
31	Depreciation exp.					0	0				
32	Wages payable					0	0				
34				FORMUL1	FORMUL2	FORMUL3	FORMUL4	FORMUL5	FORMUL6	FORMUL7	FORMUL8
36	Net income							0	0	0	0
39								0	0	0	0

P3 MERCHANDISING WORKSHEET (WSHEET2)

STUDENT NAME _____

SECTION NUMBER _____

The trial balance of Crossman Bookstore at March 31, 19X4, the end of the current fiscal year, is as follows:

Crossman Bookstore
Trial Balance
March 31, 19X4

Cash	$ 4,045	
Accounts Receivable	9,260	
Merchandise Inventory	15,988	
Prepaid Insurance	1,470	
Store Supplies	790	
Store Equipment	10,000	
Accumulated Depreciation		$ 1,000
Accounts Payable		4,139
B. Crossman, Capital		27,520
B. Crossman, Drawing	4,800	
Sales		99,800
Purchases	64,300	
Advertising Expense	2,650	
Rent Expense	4,000	
Salaries Expense	13,280	
Utilities Expense	1,876	
	$132,459	$132,459

Adjustment information is as follows:

a. Supplies on hand, March 31, 19X4 is $150
b. Insurance premiums that expired during the year totaled $807.
c. Depreciation on equipment during the year is $500.
d. Salaries accrued but not paid at March 31, 19X4 totaled $480.
e. Merchandise inventory on March 31, 19X4 is $14,621.

Required

1) As accountant for Crossman, you have been asked to prepare adjusting entries, financial statements, and closing entries to complete the accounting cycle for the year. A template called WSHEET2 has been provided to assist you in this assignment. As you review this template, it should be noted that columns J and K will automatically change when you enter values in columns G and I.

2) There are eight formulas requested to complete the template. Using the spaces provided below, write the formulas required to complete the template.

FORMULA1 _____   FORMULA5 _____

FORMULA2 _____   FORMULA6 _____

FORMULA3 _____   FORMULA7 _____

FORMULA4 _____   FORMULA8 _____

3) Load the spreadsheet program and then load the template WSHEET2. Enter the formulas in the appropriate cells on the template. Then enter the adjusting amounts in columns G and I. Also, in column F or H insert the letter corresponding to the adjusting entry (a - e). (Note: Not all textbooks handle the change in inventory as an adjustment. Use the method for handling inventory that is prescribed in your textbook.) Columns A through C are "frozen" on the screen to assist you in completing Requirement 4 below.

4) Complete the income statement and balance sheet by entering the appropriate formulas in columns L, M, N, and O. (Do not use the copy command to accomplish this. Enter formulas referencing the appropriate cells in columns J or K.) Net income will be automatically calculated at the bottom of the income statement and balance sheet columns. Check to be sure that these numbers are the same. Save the completed template as WSHEET24. If you have an IBM or Epson printer, press ALT C to print the template in compressed mode. If not, press ALT P, and the worksheet will automatically print in two sections. *Check figure: Net income (cell L40), $9,900*

What-If Analysis

5) Suppose you discover that your boss had mistakenly provided you with wrong information on two of the adjusting entries. Expired insurance premiums should have been $870, and unpaid salaries should have been $880. Make the corrections on your worksheet and reprint it. Save the corrected file as WSHEET25.

6) On the forms below, prepare an income statement, a capital statement (statement of owner's equity), and a balance sheet. Use the corrected file (WSHEET25) as a basis for your financials. Assume no additional owner investments were made during the year.

Graphics

7) Retrieve WSHEET25 and press the F10 key. On the screen, a pie chart shows the percentage composition of the total expenses of Crossman Bookstore. Enter the percentages below. Compare the percentages of Crossman Bookstore with the national statistics provided. Comment on the differences noted. Why might depreciation, utilities, and rent (as a group) be so far off from the national percentages? Any explanation for salaries? COGS?

	National Averages	Crossman Bookstore
Cost of goods sold	65.0%	
Salaries	20.0	
Utilities	4.0	
Depreciation	4.0	
Insurance	3.0	
Supplies	2.0	
Rent	1.0	
Advertising	1.0	
	100.0%	100.0%
	=====	=====

TEMPLATE TICKLER

Include the income statement on the WSHEET25 template. Beginning on line 90 of the template, enter the income statement (headings, etc.) that was required to be handwritten in Requirement 6 of the problem. Remove the title freeze (/WTC) to allow full use of columns A, B, and C. Enter formulas in the statement to reference the appropriate cells in the adjusted trial balance columns (J and K) of the worksheet (Exception: Beginning inventory is in column D). Use proper formats for all value cells. Save the template as WSHEET2T. Print the income statement (not the whole worksheet) when done.

GRAPHICS TICKLER

Retrieve WSHEET25. Remove the freeze on columns A through C by typing /WTC. Type /Graph, Name, Create, ORIG, and press ENTER. Then press Reset and Graph. Remove the title freeze (/WTC) to allow full use of columns A, B, and C. Create a bar graph showing the dollar total of each of the expenses of Crossman Bookstore. Use B55.B62 as the X-axis and C55.C62 as the A-range. Use appropriate titles, legends, and formats. Save the graph as a PIC file called WSHEET2G. Save the template again as WSHEET25. Print the graph.

MACRO TICKLER

Retrieve WSHEET25. Create a macro named \R to print the worksheet without columns D through K showing.

WSHEET2   Student Name   =>
               Section Number =>

Crossman Bookstore
Work Sheet
For Year Ended March 31, 19X4

#	Account Title	Trial Balance Dr.	Cr.	Adjustments Dr.	Cr.	Adj. T/Balance Dr.	Cr.	Income Statement Dr.	Cr.	Balance Sheet Dr.	Cr.
13	Cash	4,045				4,045	0				
14	Accts receivable	9,260				9,260	0				
15	Merchandise inv.	15,988				15,988	0				
16	Prepaid insurance	1,470				1,470	0				
17	Store Supplies	790				790	0				
18	Store equipment	10,000				10,000	0				
19	Accum. deprec.		1,000			0	1,000				
20	Accounts payable		4,139			0	4,139				
21	Crossman, capital		27,520			0	27,520				
22	Crossman, drawing	4,800				4,800	0				
23	Sales		99,800			0	99,800				
24	Purchases	64,300				64,300	0				
25	Advertising exp.	2,650				2,650	0				
26	Rent expense	4,000				4,000	0				
27	Salaries exp.	13,280				13,280	0				
28	Utilities exp.	1,876				1,876	0				
29		-------	-------								
30		132,459	132,459								
31		=======	=======								
32	Income summary					0	0				
33	Supplies expense					0	0				
34	Insurance expense					0	0				
35	Depreciation exp.					0	0				
36	Salaries payable					0	0				
37				-------	-------	-------	-------	-------	-------	-------	-------
38				FORMUL1	FORMUL2	FORMUL3	FORMUL4	FORMUL5	FORMUL6	FORMUL7	FORMUL8
39				=======	=======	=======	=======	-------	-------	-------	-------
40	Net income							0	0	0	0
41								-------	-------	-------	-------
42								0	0	0	0
43								=======	=======	=======	=======
44											

P4 MERCHANDISING ENTERPRISE (MERCH)

STUDENT NAME _____

SECTION NUMBER _____

The following information is for Centennial Company for the month ended January 31, 19X3:

Accounts Payable	$138,000	Prepaid Insurance	$ 16,000
Accounts Receivable	149,275	Purchases	279,000
Accum. Depreciation--		Purchases Discount	36,215
Store Equipment	203,000	Rent Expense--General	3,000
Advertising Expense	22,000	Rent Expense--Selling	10,000
Bush, Capital,		Salaries Expense--	
beginning	180,000	General	12,000
Bush, Drawing	96,000	Salaries Expense--	
Cash	35,720	Selling	64,000
Depreciation Exp.	6,000	Salaries Payable	8,200
Insurance Exp.--General	600	Sales	507,000
Insurance Exp.--Selling	5,400	Sales Discount	32,000
Merchandise Inventory,		Store Equipment	250,000
beginning	78,000	Store Supplies	3,920
Merchandise Inventory,		Store Supplies Expense	9,500
ending	103,000		

Required

1) Review the template called MERCH that follows these requirements. You have been asked to prepare Centennial's financial statements using this template. Note that the data from the problem have already been entered into the top section of the worksheet. Cells which contain zeros on the template have been preprogrammed. As you enter formulas onto the template, these zeros will be replaced by values.

2) Using the spaces provided below, write the formulas and titles where requested in the template. FORMULA2 and TITLE A have been written for you as examples.

FORMULA1 _____   FORMULA11 _____

FORMULA2 _____+H29_____   FORMULA12 _____

FORMULA3 _____   FORMULA13 _____

FORMULA4 _____   FORMULA14 _____

FORMULA5 _____   FORMULA15 _____

FORMULA6 _____   FORMULA16 _____

FORMULA7 _____   FORMULA17 _____

FORMULA8 _____   FORMULA18 _____

FORMULA9 _____   FORMULA19 _____

FORMULA10 _____   FORMULA20 _____

TITLE A _____Sales discount_____   TITLE G _____

TITLE B _____   TITLE H _____

TITLE C _____   TITLE I _____

TITLE D _____   TITLE J _____

TITLE E _____   TITLE K _____

TITLE F _____   TITLE L _____

3) Load the spreadsheet program and then load the template MERCH. Enter all formulas and titles where indicated on the template. When you are finished, make sure that your balance sheet balances! Save your completed model as MERCH3. Use ALT P to print the results when done. *Check figure: Net income (cell H78), $124,715*

What-If Analysis

4) To test your model, enter the following data in the Data Section for the month of February.

Accounts Payable	$105,000	Prepaid Insurance	$ 9,450
Accounts Receivable	132,800	Purchases	267,000
Accum. Depreciation--		Purchases Discount	20,000
Store Equipment	211,000	Rent Expense--General	3,000
Advertising Expense	48,000	Rent Expense--Selling	10,000
Bush, Capital,		Salaries Expense--	
beginning	208,715	General	18,000
Bush, Drawing	85,000	Salaries Expense--	
Cash	25,175	Selling	80,000
Depreciation Exp.	8,000	Salaries Payable	4,600
Insurance Exp.--General	650	Sales	575,000
Insurance Exp.--Selling	5,900	Sales Discount	25,000
Merchandise Inventory,		Store Equipment	290,000
beginning	103,000	Store Supplies	2,240
Merchandise Inventory,		Store Supplies Expense	11,100
ending	62,000		

When you are finished, make sure your balance sheet balances. Save your completed template as MERCH4. Use ALT P to print the results when done.

5) Compare the January and February income statements. Comment on any trends noted.

_____
_____
_____
_____
_____
_____
_____
_____
_____
_____
_____

Graphics

6) Retrieve MERCH4 and press F10. You will see a line graph depicting the five month trend in sales, gross profit, and net income. What favorable and unfavorable trends do you see in this month-to-month comparison? Comment on any unusual changes.

_____

_____

_____

_____

_____

_____

_____

TEMPLATE TICKLER

Retrieve MERCH4. Your boss would prefer to have the selling and general expenses on the income statement listed in descending numerical order. Please make this change. Save the revised template as MERCHT. Print the results when done.

GRAPHICS TICKLER

Retrieve MERCH4. Type /Graph, Name, Create, **ORIG**, and press ENTER. Then press **Reset** and **Graph**. Prepare a bar graph which shows the amount of each of the selling expenses in February. No graphics data table is needed. Use B61 to B66 as the X-axis (shorten titles to fit) and F61 to F66 as the A-range. Save the graph as a PIC file called MERCHG. Save the template again as MERCH4. Print the graph.

MACRO TICKLER

Design a print macro named \R on the MERCH4 template to print only the Answer Section of the template with each financial statement on a separate page.

Student Name   =
Section Number =

A	B	C	D	E	F	G	H

6	Data Section:					Month:	January
7							
8	Accounts Payable						$138,000
9	Accounts Receivable						149,275
10	Accumulated Depreciation-Store Equipment						203,000
11	Advertising Expense						22,000
12	Bush, Capital - beginning						180,000
13	Bush, Drawing						96,000
14	Cash						35,720
15	Depreciation Expense-Store Equipment						6,000
16	Insurance Expense-General						600
17	Insurance Expense-Selling						5,400
18	Merchandise Inventory, beginning						78,000
19	Merchandise Inventory, ending						103,000
20	Prepaid Insurance						16,000
21	Purchases						279,000
22	Purchases Discount						36,215
23	Rent Expense-General						3,000
24	Rent Expense-Selling						10,000
25	Salaries Expense-General						12,000
26	Salaries Expense-Selling						64,000
27	Salaries Payable						8,200
28	Sales						507,000
29	Sales Discount						32,000
30	Store Equipment						250,000
31	Store Supplies						3,920
32	Store Supplies Expense						9,500
33							

```
34 Answer Section:
35
36                     Centennial Company
37                     Income Statement
38              For Month Ended January 31, 19X3
39
40 Revenue:
41    Sales                                      FORMULA1
42    Less:   TITLE A                            FORMULA2
43                                               --------
44      Net sales                                           FORMULA3
45 Cost of goods sold:
46    Beginning merchandise inventory                 $0
47    TITLE B                          FORMULA4
48    Less:   TITLE C                  FORMULA5
49                                     --------
50    Net purchases                                   FORMULA6
51                                                    --------
52    Goods available for sale                        $0
53    Less ending inventory                           FORMULA7
54                                                    --------
55      Cost of goods sold                                  FORMULA8
56                                                          --------
57 TITLE D                                                  $0
58
59 Operating expenses:
60    Selling expenses:
61       TITLE E                       FORMULA9
62       Depr. expense-store equipment        0
63       Insurance expense-selling            0
64       Rent expense-selling                 0
65       TITLE F                       FORMULA10
66       TITLE G                       FORMULA11
67                                     --------
68         Total selling expenses                    $0
69    General expenses:
70       Insurance expense-general            $0
71       Rent expense-general                 0
72       TITLE H                       FORMULA12
73                                     --------
74         Total general expenses                    0
75                                                    --------
76    Total operating expenses                               0
77                                                           --------
78 Net income                                                FORMULA13
79                                                           ========
80 --------------------------------------------------------------------
81
```

```
 82                   Centennial Company
 83                   Capital Statement
 84             For Month Ended January 31, 19X3
 85
 86 Beginning balance, capital                                    $0
 87 Net income                          FORMULA14
 88 TITLE I                             FORMULA15
 89                                     --------
 90 Change in capital                                      FORMULA16
 91                                                        --------
 92 Ending balance, capital                                        $0
 93                                                        ========
 94 ----------------------------------------------------------------
 95
 96                   Centennial Company
 97                     Balance Sheet
 98                    January 31, 19X3
 99
100                         Assets
101 Current assets:
102    Cash                                     $0
103    Accounts receivable                       0
104    TITLE J                       FORMULA17
105    Store supplies                            0
106    Prepaid insurance                         0
107                                     --------
108     Total current assets                                       $0
109 Fixed assets:
110    TITLE K                       FORMULA18
111    Less accumulated depr.-store equipment    0
112                                     --------
113     Total fixed assets                                          0
114                                                        --------
115 Total assets                                                   $0
116                                                        ========
117                   Liabilities & Capital
118 Liabilities:
119    Accounts payable                         $0
120    TITLE L                       FORMULA19
121                                     --------
122     Total liabilities                                          $0
123 Capital:
124    Bush, capital                                       FORMULA20
125                                                        --------
126 Total liabilities & capital                                    $0
127                                                        ========
128 ----------------------------------------------------------------
```

P5 PURCHASES JOURNAL
(PJOURNAL)

STUDENT NAME _____

SECTION NUMBER_____

During the month of April, Sparrow Industries completed the following purchases on account and the related returns and allowances:

April

1   Purchased merchandise on account from Mainco, $4,260.
3   Purchased store supplies on account from Lincoln Supply Co., $885.
4   Purchased merchandise on account from Valdez Inc., $2,674.
5   Purchased office equipment on account from CXP Equipment, $1,700.
10 Received a credit memorandum from Mainco for merchandise returned, $510.
11 Purchased store supplies on account from Print 'n Go, $476.
15 Received a credit memorandum on account from Valdez Inc. as an allowance for damaged merchandise, $219.
17 Purchased merchandise on account from Baks Distributors, $7,210.
19 Purchased merchandise on account from Valdez Inc., $1,867.
21 Received a credit memorandum from Print 'n Go for store supplies returned, $72.
22 Purchased store supplies on account from Lincoln Supply Co., $720.

Required

1) You have been asked to record these transactions using a purchases journal and a general journal. The template called PJOURNAL is a computerized purchases journal. Since purchases journals vary in format, review the PJOURNAL template now. Sparrow Industries uses its purchases journal to record all acquisitions made on account including inventory, supplies, and equipment. Returns and allowances are recorded in the general journal. Note that formulas are required for the totals.

2) In the spaces provided below, enter the four formulas required.

FORMULA1 _____   FORMULA3 _____

FORMULA2 _____   FORMULA4 _____

3) Load the spreadsheet program and then load the template PJOURNAL. Enter the formulas in the appropriate cells on the template. Then record the transactions in the purchases journal or in the general journal shown below. Use the general journal only for transactions not entered in the purchases journal. The first transaction in the purchases journal has been recorded for you. When you are finished, save the results as PJAPR and use ALT P to print the template. *Check figure: Total credits to accounts payable (cell D27), $19,792*

JOURNAL   PAGE

	DATE	DESCRIPTION	POST. REF.	DEBIT	CREDIT	
1						1
2						2
3						3
4						4
5						5
6						6

4) Assume that Sparrow Industries uses an accounts payable subsidiary ledger. In the space provided below, describe to a colleague how the journal is to be posted. Provide details.

_____

_____

_____

_____

_____

What-If Analysis

5) Erase the transactions recorded in PJAPR (using the /RE command) and record the following transactions which occurred in May:

May
1   Purchased store supplies on account from Print 'n Go, $135.
5   Purchased merchandise on account from Valdez Inc., $3,820.
7   Purchased merchandise on account form Mesa Products, $9,200.
13 Purchased store equipment on account from Romano's, $600.
22 Purchased merchandise on account from Valdez Inc., $2,200.
27 Purchased store supplies on account from Lincoln Supply Co., $1,120.

Save the results as PJMAY. Use ALT P to print the May template.

Graphics

6) Judy Sparrow, the owner of Sparrow Industries, has been advised that as a rule of thumb she should keep her supplies purchases to less that 10% of her total supplies and merchandise purchases. Retrieve PJAPR and press the F10 key. Is the goal met in April? Retrieve the PJMAY template and press the F10 key. Is the goal met in May?

_____

_____

_____

_____

_____

TEMPLATE TICKLER

Retrieve the PJAPR template. At the present time, Sparrow Industries only sells sports equipment. However, the owner has decided to expand the business by also selling uniforms, swim suits, golf clothes, etc. Modify the template to include two categories of purchases: use the current column for equipment purchases and add a new column for clothing purchases. Then record the entry for the following transaction:

Apr. 29   Purchased merchandise on account from Valdez Inc.:

clothes, $2,000; equipment, $900.

When finished, print the template using B1 to I37 as the print range. Save the completed template as PJOURNAT.

Hint: To accommodate a new category of purchases, remove the worksheet protection, move the cursor to column F, insert a new column, and enter a proper heading. In the new cell F27, enter a formula that will total that column. Modify the formula for Total Debits on line 32.

GRAPHICS TICKLER

Retrieve the PJAPR template. Type /Graph, Name, Create, **ORIG**, and press ENTER. Do not reset the graph. Create a bar graph showing the dollars of merchandise purchases and supplies purchases. Give the graph an appropriate title and properly format the Y-axis. Save the graph as a PIC file called PJAPRG. Save the template again as PJAPR. Print the graph.

Hint: Use the same X-axis and A-range as ORIG. Change the graph type from pie to bar.

MACRO TICKLER

Retrieve the PJAPR template. Create a macro named \R which will erase the entries on the purchase journal template at the end of each month so that new monthly data can be entered on a "clean" template. The range to be erased each month is B15 to H25.

```
PJOURNAL                    Student Name      =
                            Section Number    =
------------------------------------------------------------------------
A    B           C           D       E       F       G           H
------------------------------------------------------------------------
 6
 7
 8                            Purchases Journal              Page 4
 9  --------------------------------------------------------------------
10                                                   Sundry Accounts Dr.
11                            Accts.          Store   --------------------
12                            Pay.    Purch.  Supp.    Account
13  Date  Account Credited    Cr.     Dr.     Dr.       Name      Amount
14  --------------------------------------------------------------------
15  April
16     1 Mainco               4,260   4,260
17
18
19
20
21
22
23
24
25
26                            -------  ------  ------              ------
27  Totals                    FORMU1  FORMU2  FORMU3              FORMU4
28                            ======  ======  ======              ======
29
30
31                                            ----------------------------
32                                            Total debits             0
33                                            Total credits            0
34                                                               ------
35                                            Difference               0
36                                                               ======
37  --------------------------------------------------------------------
```

P6 BANK RECONCILIATION (BANKREC)

STUDENT NAME _____

SECTION NUMBER _____

Ed's Bait & Tackle deposits all receipts in a night depository after banking hours. The data needed to reconcile the bank statement as of October 31 have been extracted from records and are as follows:

From Ed's records:

Checking account balance as of October 1	$8,210.57
Cash received and deposited in October (detail below*)	4,628.05
Checks written during October (detail below**)	- 5,138.92
Checkbook balance as of October 31	$7,699.70
	=======

* Date and amount of each deposit in October: Oct. 3, $620.45; Oct. 8, $962.00; Oct. 11, $746.92; Oct. 16, $525.27; Oct. 19, $671.35; Oct. 24, $843.00; Oct. 28, $259.06.

** Number and amount of each check issued in October:

No.	Amount	No.	Amount	No.	Amount	No.	Amount
840	$316.90	844	$986.25	848	$266.40	852	$326.47
841	46.17	845	714.68	849	Void	853	Void
842	246.81	846	165.20	850	78.59	854	120.00
843	91.50	847	472.53	851	790.72	855	516.70

From October's bank statement:

Balance as of October 1	$ 9,060.63
Deposits recorded in October (detail below*)	4,685.89
Checks charged to account in October (detail below**)	- 4,591.64
Other adjustments (detail below***)	1,181.60
Balance as of October 31	$10,336.48
	========

* Date and amount of each deposit in October: Oct. 1, $316.90; Oct. 4, $620.45; Oct. 9, $962.00; Oct. 12, $746.92; Oct. 17, $525.27; Oct. 20, $671.35; Oct. 25, $843.00.

** Number and amount of each check in October:

No.	Amount	No.	Amount	No.	Amount	No.	Amount
830	$ 60.90	841	$ 46.17	845	$741.68	848	$266.40
837	271.45	842	246.81	846	165.20	850	78.59
838	520.79	843	91.50	847	472.53	852	326.47
840	316.90	844	986.25				

***Description of each memo accompanying October's bank statement:

Date	Description	Amount
Oct. 4	Bank debit memo for check returned because of insufficient funds	$ 62.40
Oct. 12	Bank credit memo for note collected:	
	Principal	1,200.00
	Interest	50.00
Oct. 31	Bank debit memo for service charges	6.00

Required

1) As treasurer, you have been asked to prepare a bank reconciliation as of October 31. Review the template called BANKREC that follows these requirements. The bank reconciliation as of September 30 is provided for you as a sample completed template. You may need to refer to the September 30 bank reconciliation for information on outstanding checks.

2) Using the spaces provided below, write the formulas where requested in the template. Carefully review the September 30 template printout and note that subtractions are entered as negative numbers.

FORMULA1 _____   FORMULA3 _____

FORMULA2 _____

3) Load the spreadsheet program and then load the template BANKREC. Enter the formulas where indicated on the template. Prepare a bank reconciliation as of October 31. Assume that all errors are the depositor's fault. The reconciliation is not complete until the difference between the adjusted balances (cell H43) is zero. Save your completed template as BANKREC3. Use ALT P to print the template when done. *Check figure: Adjusted balance (cell H24), $8,854.30*

4) On the form below, prepare the necessary adjusting journal entries.

JOURNAL   PAGE

	DATE	DESCRIPTION	POST. REF.	DEBIT	CREDIT	
1						1
2						2
3						3
4						4
5						5
6						6
7						7
8						8
9						9
10						10
11						11
12						12
13						13
14						14
15						15
16						16
17						17
18						18

What-If Analysis

5) Retrieve the BANKREC3 template. Erase all October data and use the template to complete the following bank reconciliation:

Ed's Bait & Tackle
Bank Reconciliation
November 30, 19X8

Book balance of cash	?	Bank statement balance		6,990
Add: Collection of note	700	Add: Deposit in transit		?
Interest earned	50	Bank error		30
	7,870			?
Deduct: Service charge	12	Deduct: Checks outstanding		457
NSF check	?			
Adjusted balance	6,702	Adjusted balance		
	====			====

Save your completed template as BANKREC5. Use ALT P to print the results.

Graphics

6) Retrieve the BANKREC3 template. Press the F10 key. On the screen, a bar graph appears illustrating relative book and bank balances at July 31 and August 31. In the space provided below, list at least two reasons why the discrepancy between book and bank balances may have existed at July 31.

a. _____

b. _____

c. _____

d. _____

Why may it have existed at August 31?

a. _____

b. _____

c. _____

d. _____

TEMPLATE TICKLER

Retrieve the BANKREC template. Suppose that there are eight checks outstanding at the end of December, 19X8. Modify the template to accept additional outstanding checks. Save the completed template as BANKRECT. Print the template when done.

GRAPHICS TICKLER

Retrieve the BANKREC5 template. Type /Graph, Name, Create, **ORIG**, and press ENTER. Then press **Reset** and **Graph**. Prepare a line graph to show the monthly ending book and bank balance from July 31 through November 30. Use the graphics data table in rows 57 and 58 as a basis for preparing the graph. Expand the table to include data for September, October, and November. Use B57.B61 as the X-axis, E57.E61 as the A-range, and F57.F61 as the B-range. Save the graph as a PIC file called BANKRECG. Save the template again as BANKREC5. Print the graph.

MACRO TICKLER

Create a macro named \R on the BANKREC3 template to use at the end of each month to erase all labels, dates, and data from the template and leave it "clean" for the next month.

```
BANKREC                Student Name   =
                       Section Number =
   ------------------------------------------------------------------
   A      B        C        D        E        F        G        H
   ------------------------------------------------------------------
 6
 7                          Ed's Bait & Tackle
 8                          Bank Reconciliation
 9                          October 31, 19X8
10 ------------------------------------------------------------------
11 Balance per bank statement                               $.00
12 Additions by depositor not on bank statement:
13
14
15 Deductions by depositor not on bank statement:
16
17
18
19
20 Bank errors:
21
22
23                                                        ---------
24 Adjusted balance                                        FORMULA1
25                                                        =========
26 ------------------------------------------------------------------
27 Balance per books                                        $.00
28 Additions by bank not recorded by depositor:
29
30
31
32 Deductions by bank not recorded by depositor:
33
34
35
36 Depositor's errors:
37
38
39                                                        ---------
40 Adjusted balance                                        FORMULA2
41                                                        =========
42 ------------------------------------------------------------------
43 Difference between adjusted balances                     FORMULA3
44                                                        =========
45 ------------------------------------------------------------------
```

Student Name   = September 30
Section Number =

A	B	C	D	E	F	G	H

```
 6
 7                      Ed's Bait & Tackle
 8                      Bank Reconciliation
 9                      September 30, 19X8
10 --------------------------------------------------------
11 Balance per bank statement                    $9,060.63
12 Additions by depositor not on bank statement:
13         Deposit in transit                       316.90
14
15 Deductions by depositor not on bank statement:
16         Checks outstanding #830                  (60.90)
17                            #837                  (271.45)
18                            #838                  (520.79)
19                            #839                  (313.82)
20 Bank errors:
21
22
23                                                 --------
24 Adjusted balance                              $8,210.57
25                                                 ========
26 --------------------------------------------------------
27 Balance per books                             $8,216.57
28 Additions by bank not recorded by depositor:
29         Note collected - principal
30         Note collected - interest
31
32 Deductions by bank not recorded by depositor:
33         Service charge                           (6.00)
34
35
36 Depositor's errors:
37
38
39                                                 --------
40 Adjusted balance                              $8,210.57
41                                                 ========
42 --------------------------------------------------------
43 Difference between adjusted balances             $.00
44                                                 ========
45 --------------------------------------------------------
```

P7 DISCOUNTED NOTES RECEIVABLE (NRDISC)

STUDENT NAME _____

SECTION NUMBER _____

Tri-State Distributors holds a 75-day, 10% note for $7,500, dated August 2, that was received from a customer on account. On August 17, the note is discounted at the First National Bank at the rate of 13%.

Required

1) Review the template called NRDISC. You have been asked to calculate the cash proceeds from the note when it is discounted.

2) Using the spaces provided below, write the formulas where requested in the template. Assume a 365-day year.

FORMULA1 _____   FORMULA4 _____

FORMULA2 _____   FORMULA5 _____

FORMULA3 _____

3) Load the spreadsheet program and then load the template NRDISC. Enter all the formulas where indicated on the template. Save your completed template as NRDISC3. Use ALT P to print the template when done. *Check figure: Cash proceeds (cell G23), $7,491*

4) On the form below, prepare a journal entry to record the discounting transaction.

JOURNAL

PAGE _____

	DATE	DESCRIPTION	POST. REF.	DEBIT	CREDIT	
1						1
2						2
3						3
4						4
5						5
6						6
7						7
8						8
9						9
10						10
11						11
12						12
13						13
14						14
15						15
16						16

What-If Analysis

5) Change the input data to show a discount period of 20 days. Why do the proceeds exceed the face value in this case, whereas in Requirement 3 it didn't?

_____

_____

_____

_____

6) Suppose the Tri-State Distributors holds the note for only one day and then discounts it at the bank for 10%. To determine the cash proceeds, change the input data to show a bank interest rate of 10% and a discount period of 74 days. Why are the proceeds less than the face value in spite of the fact that the bank is charging the same rate as the note itself?

_____

_____

_____

_____

Graphics

7) Retrieve the NRDISC3 template. Press the F10 key. In the space provided below, describe what is being illustrated by this graph. Identify what the A-range is (the squares); what the B-range is (the crosses); and what the X-axis is.

_____

_____

_____

_____

_____

8) a. On the X-axis, where is the approximate intersection of the two ranges?

_____

   b. Press ENTER, change the stated interest to 12% (cell G9), and press F10 again. What happens to the intersection of the two ranges? Why?

_____

_____

_____

_____

TEMPLATE TICKLER

Retrieve the NRDISC3 template. The bank has a discount rate of 13%, but the true cost to Tri-State Distributors is greater than that because the discount rate is applied to the maturity value whereas the company only "borrows" the cash proceeds. The true interest rate can be computed by dividing the bank discount (cell G21) by the cash proceeds (cell G23) and then annualizing the rate over 365 days. Modify the template to perform this computation in cell G26. Save the completed template as NRDISCT. Print the results when done.

GRAPHICS TICKLER

Retrieve the NRDISC3 template. Do not reset the graph. However, type /Graph, Name, Create, ORIG, and press ENTER to name the original graph. Press **V** to View. Note that the graph shown is lacking titles, legends, etc. You are to spruce up this graph by adding a title at the top, a title for the X-axis, legends for the A and B ranges, and format the values on the Y-axis using dollar signs. Save the graph as a PIC file called NRDISCG. Save the template again as NRDISC3. Print the graph.

MACRO TICKLER

Develop a macro named \R on the NRDISC3 template to print the template without any row numbers or headings showing. In other words, the print range is B6 to H25.

Student Name   =
                        Section Number =

A   B   C   D   E   F   G   H
----

 6 Data Section:
 7
 8 Face value of note $7,500
 9 Stated interest rate on note   10%
10 Term of note   75 days
11 Bank interest rate   13%
12 Discount period   60 days
13
14 --
15 Answer Section:
16
17 Face value of note   FORMULA1
18 Interest to maturity   FORMULA2
19   --------
20 Maturity value   FORMULA3
21 Bank discount   FORMULA4
22   --------
23 Cash proceeds   FORMULA5
24   ========
25 --

P8 AGING ACCOUNTS RECEIVABLE (AGING)

STUDENT NAME _____

SECTION NUMBER _____

On November 30, 19X6, Data Destruction Inc., an on-site mobile paper shredding service, had the following amounts due from its customers:

Customer	Total	Not Yet Due	1-30 Days Past Due	31-60 Days Past Due	61-90 Days Past Due	Over 90 Days Past Due
J. R. Ewing	$2,300	$1,800	$ 150			$ 350
Miami Advice	4,750	3,900	850			
Mudd & Mudd	4,000	1,000	1,000	$1,000	$1,000	
RMN Plumbing	900	900				
Ollie's Inc.	300					300
R. Reagan	1,988		400	258	800	530
Totals	$14,238	$7,600	$2,400	$1,258	$1,800	$1,180
	======	=====	=====	=====	=====	=====

Based on the company's past experience, it has established the following percentages for estimating uncollectible accounts:

Age Interval	Percent Uncollectible
Not yet due	1%
1-30 days past due	3
31-60 days past due	5
61-90 days past due	10
Over 90 days past due	25

Required

1) You have been asked to estimate the total amount of uncollectible accounts expense as of November 30 by completing the template called AGING.

2) Using the spaces provided below, write the formulas where requested in the template. FORMULA1 has been done for you as an example.

FORMULA1 _____+D21_____   FORMULA7 _____

FORMULA2 _____   FORMULA8 _____

FORMULA3 _____   FORMULA9 _____

FORMULA4 _____   FORMULA10 _____

FORMULA5 _____   FORMULA11 _____

FORMULA6 _____   FORMULA12 _____

3) Load the spreadsheet program and then load the template AGING. Enter all formulas where indicated on the template. Save your completed template as AGING3. Use ALT P to print the results when done. *Check figure: Total uncollectible (cell H37), $686*

4) Assume that November's sales were $55,000. On the forms provided below, record the journal entry for the provision for uncollectible accounts under each of the following independent assumptions:

a. The Allowance for Doubtful Accounts before adjustment has a credit balance of $400.

b. The Allowance for Doubtful Accounts before adjustment has a debit balance of $150.

c. Uncollectible accounts expense is estimated at 2% of sales.

What-If Analysis

5) Retrieve AGING3. Erase the aging information for November (using the /RE command) and enter the following information for December 31, 19X6:

Customer	Total	Not Yet Due	1-30 Days Past Due	31-60 Days Past Due	61-90 Days Past Due	Over 90 Days Past Due
J. R. Ewing	$ 2,550	$1,600	$ 800	$ 150		
M. Gorbachev	2,000	2,000				
Mudd & Mudd	5,000	1,000	1,000	1,000	$1,000	$1,000
Ollie's Inc.	300					300
R. Reagan	3,158	1,700		400	258	800
Welltech	5,700	5,700				
Totals	$18,708	$12,000	$1,800	$1,550	$1,258	$2,100

Save the results as AGING5. Use ALT P to print the template. Has the estimated total uncollectible accounts increased or decreased in December? Explain.

_____

_____

_____

_____

_____

Graphics

6) a. With AGING5 still on the screen, press the F10 key. Describe what is being plotted out on this graph.

_____

_____

_____

_____

b. Compare the pattern to the graph for AGING3. Note any trends below.

_____

_____

_____

_____

TEMPLATE TICKLER

Retrieve the AGING5 template. Suppose that there had been one additional customer with a balance due at December 31. This customer's name was Palo Pugliesi, and he owed $1,200 which was not yet due. Alter the template to allow entry of this information in alphabetic order and modify any affected formulas. Save the completed template as AGINGT. Print the results when done.

GRAPHICS TICKLER

Retrieve the AGING3 template. Type /Graph, Name, Create, **ORIG**, and press ENTER. Then press Reset and Graph. Develop a bar graph to show the total estimated uncollectible amounts (in dollars) for each age category. No graphics data table is needed; use D10.H10 as the X-Axis and H31.H35 as the A-range. Save the graph as a PIC file called AGINGG. Save the template again as AGING3. Print the graph.

MACRO TICKLER

Retrieve the AGING3 template. Create a macro named \R which will erase the entries in the top section of the template at the end of each month so that new monthly data can be entered on a "clean" template.

Student Name   =
Section Number =

```
--------------------------------------------------------------------
 A      B            C       D       E        F        G        H
--------------------------------------------------------------------
 6                                           Date: November 30, 19X6
 7
 8              Analysis of Accounts Receivable by Age
 9              -------------------------------------------
10                             Not      1-30     31-60    61-90   Over 90
11                             Yet      Days     Days     Days     Days
12    Customer      Total      Due    Past Due Past Due Past Due Past Due
13   -----------   -------   -------  -------- -------- -------- --------
14 J.R. Ewing      $2,300    $1,800    $150                      $350
15 Miami Advice     4,750     3,900     850
16 Mudd & Mudd      4,000     1,000   1,000     1,000    1,000
17 RMN Plumbing       900       900
18 Ollie's Inc.       300                                         300
19 R. Reagan        1,988                400      258      800    530
20                 -------   -------  -------- -------- -------- --------
21 Totals         $14,238    $7,600   $2,400   $1,258   $1,800   $1,180
22                 =======   =======  ======== ======== ======== ========
23
24
25
26       Estimate of Probable Uncollectible Accounts Expense
27       ---------------------------------------------------------
28                                    Total    Percent  Total
29                                    Amount   Uncoll.  Uncoll.
30                                    ------   -------  -------
31 Not yet due                        FORMULA1     1%FORMULA7
32 1-30 days past due                 FORMULA2     3%FORMULA8
33 31-60 days past due                FORMULA3     5%FORMULA9
34 61-90 days past due                FORMULA4    10%FORMULA10
35 Over 90 days past due              FORMULA5    25%FORMULA11
36                                    -------      -------
37 Totals                             FORMULA6        FORMULA12
38                                    ========      ========
39  ----------------------------------------------------------------
```

P9 GROSS PROFIT METHOD (GP)

STUDENT NAME _____

SECTION NUMBER _____

On September 30, 19X8, the general ledger of Dynamic Liquids Inc., which uses the calendar year as their accounting period, showed the following year-to-date account balances:

Sales	$570,500
Sales returns and allowances	12,000
Purchases	500,000
Purchases returns and allowances	20,000

In addition, the merchandise inventory account had a $79,900 debit balance on January 1, 19X8. The historical gross profit percentage is 25%.

Required

1) Review the template called GP. Dynamic Liquids Inc. prepares quarterly financial statements and takes physical inventory once a year, at the end of the accounting period. In order to prepare the financial statements for the third quarter, the store needs to have an estimate of ending inventory. You have been asked to estimate the ending inventory by completing the template.

2) Using the spaces provided below, write the formulas where requested in the template.

FORMULA1 _____   FORMULA5 _____

FORMULA2 _____   FORMULA6 _____

FORMULA3 _____   FORMULA7 _____

FORMULA4 _____

3) Load the spreadsheet program and then load the template GP. Enter all the formulas where indicated on the template. Save your completed worksheet as GP3. Use ALT P to print the template when done. *Check figure: Estimated ending inventory (cell H27), $141,025*

What-If Analysis

4) On December 31, 19X8, the year-to-date account balances of selected accounts were as follows:

Sales	$901,000
Sales returns and allowances	21,000
Purchases	750,000
Purchases returns and allowances	26,000

Estimated ending merchandise inventory at December 31, 19X8 is

$_____.

5) A physical count of merchandise inventory on December 31, 19X8 revealed inventory costing $135,000. In the space below, list at least two possible reasons for this balance to be different from the estimate in Requirement 4.

_____

_____

Graphics

6) Press the F10 key. The line graph that appears plots quarterly sales, gross profit, and the gross profit percentage for Dynamic Liquids. Examine the pattern of behavior for each of these three items and comment on any favorable or unfavorable trends noted.

_____

_____

_____

_____

_____

_____

_____

_____

_____

TEMPLATE TICKLER

Retrieve the GP3 template. At the present time, Dynamic Liquids Inc. includes transportation-in charges in the purchases account. On the advice of an accountant, Dynamic Liquids Inc. will establish a separate account for transportation-in charges in 19X9. Modify the template to accept this additional item of input. Then estimate ending merchandise inventory at March 31, 19X9 using the following data and print the template when done:

Sales	$250,000
Sales returns and allowances	5,500
Purchases	201,000
Purchases returns and allowances	8,200
Transportation-in	2,000
Beginning inventory (12/31/X8)	135,000
Gross profit percent (historical)	24%

Save the completed template as GPT. Print the results.

GRAPHICS TICKLER

Retrieve the GP3 template. Type /Graph, Name, Create, **ORIG**, and press ENTER. Then press **Reset** and **Graph**. Create a line graph which demonstrates the relationship between gross profit percentage and estimated ending inventory. Complete the graphics data table in columns G and H (rows 36-46) and use it as a basis for preparing the graph. Use G38.G46 as the X-axis and H38.H46 as the A-range. Save the graph as a PIC file called GPG. Save the template again as GP3. Print the graph.

MACRO TICKLER

Develop a macro named **\R** on the GP3 template to print the Answer Section before printing the Data Section.

```
GP                    Student Name   =
                      Section Number =
------------------------------------------------------------------------
   A      B       C       D       E       F       G        H
------------------------------------------------------------------------
  6 Data Section:
  7
  8 Sales                                        $570,500
  9 Sales returns and allowances                  12,000
 10 Purchases                                    500,000
 11 Purchases returns and allowances              20,000
 12 Beginning inventory                           79,900
 13 Gross profit percent (historical)              25%
 14
 15 ----------------------------------------------------------------
 16 Answer Section:
 17
 18 Beginning inventory                                    FORMULA1
 19 Net purchases                                          FORMULA2
 20                                                        --------
 21 Cost of goods available for sale                       FORMULA3
 22 Net sales                               FORMULA4
 23 Cost of goods sold percentage           FORMULA5
 24                                         --------
 25 Estimated cost of goods sold                           FORMULA6
 26                                                        --------
 27 Estimated ending inventory                             FORMULA7
 28                                                        ========
 29 ----------------------------------------------------------------
```

103

P10 DEPRECIATION
(DEPREC)

STUDENT NAME _____

SECTION NUMBER _____

Whippell Production Company recently acquired a new machine at a cost of $168,000. The machine has an estimated salvage value of $13,500 and a useful life of five years.

Required

1) Whippell buys equipment frequently, and wants to print a depreciation schedule for each asset's life. Review the template called DEPREC that follows these requirements. Since some assets acquired are depreciated straight-line, others by sum-of-the-years-digits, and others by double-declining balance, DEPREC shows all three methods. This allows the company to assess the pattern of depreciation over the asset's life. You are to use this template to prepare depreciation schedules for the new machine.

2) Using the spaces provided below, write the formulas requested. Be sure to use cell references wherever possible in your formulas instead of numbers. FORMULA1 has been written for you as an example. Since your formulas should be flexible enough to allow for different data, use the following formula as the denominator in the sum-of-the-year-digits calculation: N*(N+1)/2; where N equals the estimated life. Assume that all assets acquired will have at least a three year life. Note that all cells on the template containing zeros have been preprogrammed to perform depreciation calculations.

FORMULA1 ____(F8-F9)/F10____	FORMULA5 _____
FORMULA2 _____	FORMULA6 _____
FORMULA3 _____	FORMULA7 _____
FORMULA4 _____	FORMULA8 _____

3) Load the spreadsheet program and then load the template DEPREC. Enter the formulas in the appropriate cells. Save the completed template as DEPREC3. Use ALT P to print the template when done. *Check figure: DDB depreciation for Year 3 (cell G23), $24,192*

4) On the form below, prepare the journal entry to record the depreciation taken in Year 3 under the sum-of-the-years-digits method.

	JOURNAL				PAGE

	DATE	DESCRIPTION	POST. REF.	DEBIT	CREDIT	
1						1
2						2
3						3
4						4
5						5
6						6
7						7
8						8
9						9

What-If Analysis

5) To test your formulas, assume a machine is purchased at a cost of $85,000, has a salvage value of $4,000, and has an estimated useful life of three years. Enter the new information in the Data Section of the template. Does your depreciation total $81,000 under all three methods?

Hint: If your double-declining-balance method is off, check cell G23 where FORMULA8 is located. It should include an @IF statement which will enter a modified calculation of depreciation *if* Year 3 is the last year of the asset's expected life. Correct the formula to solve the problem. If DEPREC3 contains incorrect formulas, correct that template as well.

6) One more machine was recently bought for $225,000 with a salvage value of $20,000 and estimated useful life of 10 years. Enter the new information in the Data Section of the template. Again make sure the totals for all three methods are in agreement. Save this new data as DEPREC6. Using the information from the DEPREC6 template, plot the pattern of depreciation expense for each of the three depreciation methods on the grid below.

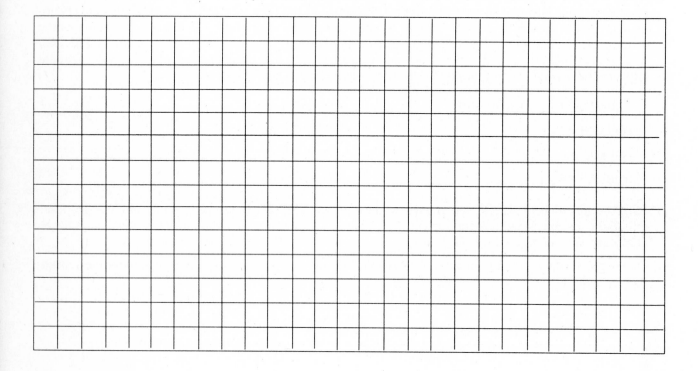

Graphics

7) The double-declining-balance method is often claimed to be the method providing the highest initial depreciation expense. This is generally true for the first few years of an asset's life, but what if a company wants to use a method which will maximize depreciation charges over an extended period of time? Is double-declining balance still best?

Retrieve the DEPREC6 template. Press the F10 key. This graph shows accumulated depreciation under all three depreciation methods over the 10-year life of the machine purchased in Requirement 6 above. Approximately, how long does double declining provide the highest accumulated write-offs?

Now let's change the scenario slightly. What happens if you change estimated salvage value from $20,000 to zero? To find out, press any key and then enter 0 in cell F9. Press the F10 key again. Approximately, how long does double-declining balance provide the highest accumulated write-offs in this case?

_____

Is double-declining balance always the best method to maximize depreciation charges? Explain.

_____

_____

_____

_____

_____

TEMPLATE TICKLER (optional)

Retrieve the DEPREC3 template. The problem thus far has assumed that assets are depreciated a full year in the year acquired. Normally, depreciation begins in the month acquired. For example, an asset acquired at the beginning of April is depreciated for only nine months in the year of acquisition. Modify the template to include the month of acquisition as an additional item of input. To demonstrate proper handling of this factor on the depreciation schedule, modify the formulas for the first two years. Be careful because some of the formulas for the second year may not actually need to be revised to provide the correct second year depreciation. Do not modify the formulas for Years 3 through 10. Use ALT P to print your modified template. Save your modified template as DEPRECT.

Hint: Insert the month in row 11 of the Data Section specifying the month by a number (April is the fourth month of the year). Redo the formulas in rows 21 and 22.

GRAPHICS TICKLER (optional)

Retrieve the DEPREC6 template. Type /Graph, Name, Create, **ORIG**, and press ENTER. Then press **Reset** and **Graph**. Prepare a line graph which plots annual depreciation expense under all three depreciation methods. The graph should look like your manual answer to Requirement 6 above. No graphics table is needed; use D21.D30 as the X-axis, E21.E30 as the A-range, F21.F30 as the B-range, and G21.G30 as the C-range. Save the graph as a PIC file called DEPRECG. Save the template again as DEPREC6. Print the graph.

MACRO TICKLER (optional)

Design three macros on the DEPREC3 template such that each would print the Data Section and only the depreciation method actually chosen for a new asset. Use \S for straight-line, \Y for sum-of-the-years-digits, and \D for double-declining balance.

DEPREC   Student Name   =
                Section Number   =

A   B   C   D   E   F   G   H   I
----
 6 Data Section:

 7

 8 Cost of asset $168,000
 9 Estimated salvage value $13,500
10 Estimated useful life   5 years

11

12 --
13 Answer Section:

14

15   Depreciation Expense
16   ---------------------------
17   Sum of   Double
18   Straight   Years   Declining
19   Year   Line   Digits   Balance
20   ----   ------------------------------
21   1 FORMULA1 FORMULA3 FORMULA6
22   2 FORMULA2 FORMULA4 FORMULA7
23   3   0 FORMULA5 FORMULA8
24   4   0   0   0
25   5   0   0   0
26   6   0   0   0
27   7   0   0   0
28   8   0   0   0
29   9   0   0   0
30   10   0   0   0
31   -------- -------- --------
32   Total $0 $0 $0
33   ======== ======== ========
34 --

STUDENT NAME _____

SECTION NUMBER _____

The Curious Antique Shop has three hourly employees and two salaried employees. Employees are paid at the end of each month. Payroll data for October are as follows:

Employee	Gross Pay for October	Federal Income Tax Withheld	Cumulative Gross Pay to September 30
Adamson	$1,592	$135	$ 5,290
Davis	1,020	201	13,450
Face	807	177	6,650
Hamilton	3,800	805	53,700
LeGray	3,400	710	46,300

Other information as is follows:

a. FICA taxes are 7.51% on monthly gross pay up to a cumulative total pay of $48,000 for each employee per year.

b. Deductions are made for medical insurance (3% of monthly gross pay) and for contributions to a pension fund (3.5% of monthly gross pay). The shop matches donations to the pension fund.

c. Unemployment taxes are paid on monthly gross pay up to the first $7,000 earned by each employee each year. State and federal rates are 2.5% and 0.7% respectively.

Required

1) You have been asked to record the payroll information using a payroll register and a general journal. Review template PR, a computerized payroll register, that follows these requirements. The columns will automatically retotal as new entries are made.

2) To make the template reusable each month, the FICA tax formulas should be designed to automatically compute whether 1) full tax is due, 2) no tax is due (e.g., cumulative gross pay is over the $48,000 ceiling), or 3) some tax is due. A double @IF statement will be required. Also, the @ROUND function should be used for Formulas 1 through 4 to eliminate rounding errors. FORMULA1 has been provided for you below. Review Appendix C and explain the meaning of each part of the formula. FORMULA1:

| ----(a)----- | --------(b)-------- | ------------------(c)------------------ | --------(d)-------- | (e) |

@ROUND(@IF(I15+48000,0,@IF((I15+C15)48000,(48000-I15)*.0751,C15*.0751)),2)

a. _____

b. _____

c. _____

d. _____

e. _____

3) In the spaces provided below, write the formulas requested.

FORMULA2 _____

FORMULA3 _____

FORMULA4 _____

FORMULA5 _____

4) Load the spreadsheet program and then load the template PR. Enter the month in cell H7. Enter the gross pay and federal income tax withheld for each employee. Then, enter the formulas where indicated on the template. As the formulas are entered, the cells that contain zeros will automatically be filled. Save the completed template as PR4. *Check figure: Total net pay (cell H21), $7,516.32*

What-If Analysis

5) The president of Curious Antique Shop has just completed a review of October sales. Because both Davis and LeGray achieved beyond their sales quotas, each is to receive an additional $200 according to their employment contracts. Increase the gross pay of each on the template by $200. Also, increase each of their federal income tax withholding by $30. The payroll register should automatically update with the new data. Save the updated template as PR5. Use ALT P to print the template. Column I will not appear on the printout.

6) On the form below, prepare the journal entry to record the October payroll assuming that the payroll is paid on October 31.

JOURNAL   PAGE

	DATE	DESCRIPTION	POST. REF.	DEBIT	CREDIT	
1						1
2						2
3						3
4						4
5						5
6						6

7) On the form below, prepare the journal entry as of October 31 to record the employer's payroll taxes and pension fund contribution, both of which will be paid on November 15.

JOURNAL   PAGE

	DATE	DESCRIPTION	POST. REF.	DEBIT	CREDIT	
1						1
2						2
3						3
4						4
5						5
6						6

Graphics

8) Retrieve the PR5 template. Press the F10 key. On the screen is a graph of the four payroll taxes that Curious Antique Shop incurs during each year. By the behaviors shown on the graph, identify below which of the four expenses each represents.

A _____

B _____

C _____

D _____

TEMPLATE TICKLER

Retrieve the PR5 template. A new employee was hired during October and was mistakenly omitted from the payroll register. The employee's last name is Rowe, and the gross pay for October is $1,000. Add the new employee to the template and include all standard withholding rates in computing net pay. Federal income tax withheld is $150. Save the completed template as PRT. Print the results when done.

GRAPHICS TICKLER

Retrieve the PR5 template. Type /Graph, Name, Create, ORIG, and press ENTER. Then press Reset and Graph. Prepare a pie graph to show the percentage of an employee's gross pay that is withheld for taxes, insurance, etc., and how much is left over as net pay. Use Davis as your example. No graphics data table is needed; use D30.H30 as the X-axis and D16.H16 as the A-range. Save the graph as a PIC file called PRG. Save the template again as PR4. Print the graph.

MACRO TICKLER

Design a macro named \R on the PR5 template to print the payroll register (range B6.I23) in compressed mode.

```
PR                      Student Name    =
                        Section Number  =
     --------------------------------------------------------------------
     A    B        C         D         E         F         G         H
     --------------------------------------------------------------------
     6                  Curious Antique Shop
     7                  Payroll Register            Month:
     8   --------------------------------------------------------------------
     9                                    Deductions
    10                       ------------------------------------------
    11                  Federal
    12                  Income    FICA                Pension
    13  Employee Gross Pay   Tax       Tax   Insurance  Fund    Net Pay
    14  --------  ---------  --------  --------  --------  --------  --------
    15  Adamson                        FORMULA1  FORMULA3  FORMULA4  FORMULA5
    16  Davis                          FORMULA2      .00       .00       .00
    17  Face                               .00       .00       .00       .00
    18  Hamilton                           .00       .00       .00       .00
    19  LeGray                             .00       .00       .00       .00
    20            ---------  --------  --------  --------  --------  --------
    21                 .00       .00       .00       .00       .00       .00
    22            =========  ========  ========  ========  ========  ========
    23  --------------------------------------------------------------------
```

P12 PARTNERSHIP
(PARTNER)

STUDENT NAME _____

SECTION NUMBER _____

Andrew Riley and Sandra Timms recently formed a partnership. Riley, who quit his old job in order to form the partnership, invested $36,000 cash, which was most of his life's savings. Timms invested $30,000 of assets and $24,000 cash. She will work part time for the business. The partners are trying to find an equitable way of dividing net income to take into account that Timms invested more capital, but Riley will spend twice as much time as Timms in running the business. The only agreement the partners have made is to divide equally any excess or deficit that is present after allowances for salary and interest. They expect net income in the first year to be $60,000, although it could range anywhere from $30,000 to $90,000. Riley has suggested the following method of dividing net income:

Interest on original investments at 10%
Salary allowances: Riley $30,000
                    Timms   15,000

Required

1) The partners would like you to experiment with different methods of dividing income to determine the effect of various interest rates, various salary allowances, and various levels of partnership income. The template PARTNER has been provided to assist you in performing this analysis.

2) Using the spaces provided below, write the formulas where requested in the template.

FORMULA1 _____   FORMULA4 _____

FORMULA2 _____   FORMULA5 _____

FORMULA3 _____   FORMULA6 _____

3) Load the spreadsheet program and then load the template PARTNER. Enter all formulas where indicated on the template. Cells that contain zeros on the template have been preprogrammed. As formulas are entered, these zeros will be replaced by values. When you are finished, make sure that total net income (cell H25) is equal to the actual net income (cell F13). Press ALT P to print the template. Save the file as PARTNER3. *Check figure: Riley's share of net income (cell F25), $36,600*

What-If Analysis

4) On the table below, record Riley's and Timms' shares if net income is $60,000. Calculate each partner's share if the net income of the partnership is $30,000 and if it is $90,000. Write the answers in the table below.

Riley's Plan

Net income	$ 30,000	$ 60,000	$ 90,000
Riley's share	$_____	$_____	$_____
Timms' share	$_____	$_____	$_____

5) Timms does not like Riley's proposed method for dividing net income, so she has suggested that net income be divided in the following manner:

Interest on original investments at 20%
Salary allowances: Riley $20,000
              Timms   10,000

Calculate each partner's share under Timms' plan for $30,000, $60,000, and $90,000 of partnership net income. Write the results in the table below.

Timms' Plan

Net income	$ 30,000	$ 60,000	$ 90,000
Riley's share	$_____	$_____	$_____
Timms' share	$_____	$_____	$_____

6) What factors should Riley and Timms consider to help them reach an agreement?

_____

_____

_____

_____

_____

_____

_____

_____

Graphics

7) Retrieve PARTNER3 and press the F10 key. This graph is based on the problem data. Answer the following questions about the graph:

a. What is the title for the X-axis? _____

b. What does the first data range (the squares) represent? _____

c. What does the second data range (the crosses) represent? _____

d. What is a good title for this graph? _____

TEMPLATE TICKLER

Assume that the partners also want to consider different profit-sharing arrangements for the "excess" other than a 50-50 split. Modify the Data Section and the Answer Section so that the effect of different sharing arrangements (e.g., 60%-40%, 90%-10%) can be examined. Note that this change will not in any way affect the formulas for the salary or interest allowances. When you are done, set the Data Section for a 60-40 split in favor of Riley and save the template as PARTNERT. Print the template. Also, print the cell contents of the revised formulas (ALT P will not work).

GRAPHICS TICKLER

Retrieve the PARTNER3 template. Do not reset the graph. However, type /Graph, Name, Create, **ORIG**, and press ENTER to name the original graph. Fix up the graph by adding the appropriate titles, legends, and formats. Save the graph as a PIC file called PARTNERG. Save the template again as PARTNER3. Print the graph.

MACRO TICKLER

Design a macro named \R on the PARTNER3 template which will rearrange the template so that the Answer Section is on top of the Data Section. The macro should then print the rearranged template.

```
PARTNER              Student Name   =
                     Section Number =
-----------------------------------------------------------------------
A     B      C       D       E       F       G       H
-----------------------------------------------------------------------
 6 Data Section:
 7
 8 Interest on original investment           10%
 9 Original investment - Riley        $36,000
10 Original investment - Timms         54,000
11 Salary allowance - Riley            30,000
12 Salary allowance - Timms            15,000
13 Net income                          60,000
14
15 -----------------------------------------------------------------------
16 Answer Section:
17                                     Riley    Timms    Total
18 Division of net income:             -----    -----    -----
19    Salary allowance               FORMULA1 FORMULA2      $0
20    Interest allowance             FORMULA3 FORMULA4       0
21                                    -------  -------  -------
22       Total                            $0       $0       $0
23    Excess of income over allowances FORMULA5 FORMULA6     0
24                                    -------  -------  -------
25 Net income                            $0       $0       $0
26                                    =======  =======  =======
27 -----------------------------------------------------------------------
```

116

P13 BOND PRICING
AND AMORTIZATION
(BONDS)

STUDENT NAME _____

SECTION NUMBER _____

Campton Corporation recently issued $1,000,000 of 10 year, 12% bonds at an effective interest rate of 13%. Bond interest is payable annually.

Required

1) You have been asked to calculate the issuance price of the bonds and prepare amortization schedules for any discount or premium. The template BONDS has been provided to assist you. Note that the template contains a Scratch Pad at the bottom which has been preprogrammed to automatically compute and display the relevant cash flows needed for bond pricing.

2) The bond pricing formula utilizes the Net Present Value function (@NPV) on your spreadsheet program. The formula is broken into two parts as identified by the numbers in parentheses above the formula. See Appendix C for a discussion on the @NPV function, and then explain the meaning of each part of the formula.

(a)   (b)

FORMULA1 @NPV(G11,C73.C84)+@NPV(G11,D73.D84)

Explanation:

a. _____

b. _____

3) Using the spaces provided below, write the formulas required to complete the template. Assume all bonds have at least a 2 year maturity. Year 0 is the date of issuance. Bond discount (column F) should be a negative number, and bond premium should be a positive number. The amortization of bond discount (column D in the straight-line table and column E in the effective interest table) should be a positive number, and the amortization of bond premium should be a negative number.

FORMULA2 _____   FORMULA14 _____

FORMULA3 _____   FORMULA15 _____

FORMULA4 _____   FORMULA16 _____

FORMULA5 _____   FORMULA17 _____

FORMULA6 _____   FORMULA18 _____

FORMULA7 _____   FORMULA19 _____

FORMULA8 _____   FORMULA20 _____

FORMULA9 _____   FORMULA21 _____

FORMULA10 _____   FORMULA22 _____

FORMULA11 _____   FORMULA23 _____

FORMULA12 _____   FORMULA24 _____

FORMULA13 _____   FORMULA25 _____

4) Load the spreadsheet program and then load the template BONDS. Enter the formulas in the appropriate cells. Save the template as BONDS4. Use ALT P to print the model when done. *Check figures: Bond issue price (cell G19), $945,738; Bond carrying value for Year 10 (cells G37 and G57), $1,000,000*

5) Prepare journal entries on the form below to record a) the issuance of the bond, b) interest expense at the end of Year 1 using the straight-line method of amortization, and c) interest expense at the end of Year 1 using the effective-interest method of amortization.

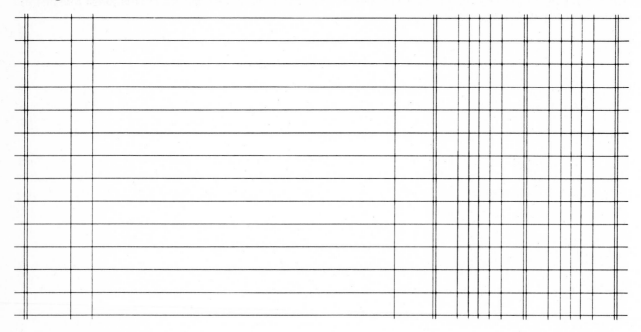

What-If Analysis

6) Use the template to compute the bond issue price and amortization schedules if the effective interest rate is 11%. Use ALT P to print the model when done. Also, repeat Requirement 5 on the form below for this bond.

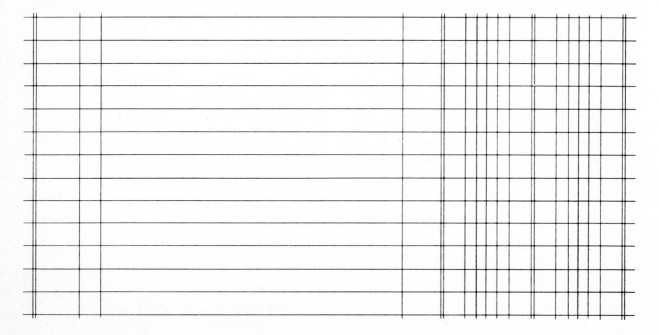

7) Use the template to compute the bond issue price if the effective interest rate is 12%.

Bond issue price $_____

8) Find the effective interest rate for $5,000,000 of 10 year, 11% bonds (interest payable annually) which were issued for $4,359,129. To do this, enter the known information in the Data Section and experiment with different effective interest rates until you get a bond price of exactly $4,359,129. (You may have to use an effective interest rate with decimals.) Use ALT P to print the template when done.

Graphics

9) a. Retrieve BONDS4. The price of this bond is $945,738. What would it be if there were only 9 or 8 years to maturity? Use the template to compute the bond issue prices and enter them below.

Bond issue price (9 years to maturity) $_____

Bond issue price (8 years to maturity) $_____

b. Compare these prices to the bond-carrying values found in the effective interest amortization schedule you originally printed out in Requirement 4 above. Explain the similarity.

_____

_____

_____

_____

_____

_____

_____

_____

c. Press the F10 key. The graph presented shows the price behavior of this bond based on years to maturity. Explain what effect years to maturity has on bond prices. Check your explanation by trying 11% as the effective rate (cell G11) and pressing F10 again. Also, try 12%.

_____

_____

_____

_____

_____

_____

_____

_____

TEMPLATE TICKLER

Retrieve the BONDS4 template. Modify the template to accommodate bonds with up to 20 year maturities. Use your new model to determine the issue price and amortization schedules of a $2,000,000, 18 year, 8% bond issued to yield 9%. Save the new model as BONDST. Print the results when done.

Hint: Expand both amortization schedules to 20 years. Expand the Scratch Pad to 20 years. Modify FORMULA1 in cell G19 to include the new ranges.

GRAPHICS TICKLER

Retrieve the BONDS4 template. Type /Graph, Name, Create, **ORIG**, and press ENTER. Then press **Reset** and **Graph**. Prepare a line graph which plots annual interest expense over the 10-year life of this bond under both the straight-line and effective interest methods. No graphics data table is needed; use B28.B37 as the X-axis, E28.E37 as the A-range, and C48.C57 as the B-range. Enter all appropriate titles, legends, formats, and so forth. Save the graph as a PIC file called BONDSG. Save the template again as BONDS4. Print the graph.

MACRO TICKLER

Develop two macros on the BONDS4 template, one of which (\S) prints the template without the effective interest method amortization schedule. The other (\E) prints the template without the straight-line method amortization schedule.

```
BONDS                   Student Name      =
                        Section Number    =
--------------------------------------------------------------------
A       B       C       D       E       F       G
--------------------------------------------------------------------
 6 Data Section:
 7
 8 Face value of bond                             $1,000,000
 9 Years to maturity *                                    10
10 Stated interest rate                                12.0%
11 Effective interest rate                            13.0%
12
13 * Template is designed for use with bonds having a maturity of
14   12 years or less and paying interest annually.
15
16 --------------------------------------------------------------------
17 Answer Section:
18
19 Bond issue price                               FORMULA1
20                                                =========
21
22 Amortization Schedule - Straight Line Method
23                                                          Bond
24               Cash    Amorti-    Interest  (Disc.)  Carrying
25       Year    Paid    zation     Expense   Premium  Value
26       ----    ----    -------    --------  -------  --------
27        0                                   FORMULA2 FORMULA3
28        1 FORMULA4  FORMULA5  FORMULA6  FORMULA7  FORMULA8
29        2 FORMULA9  FORMULA10 FORMULA11 FORMULA12 FORMULA13
30        3       0         0         0         0         0
31        4       0         0         0         0         0
32        5       0         0         0         0         0
33        6       0         0         0         0         0
34        7       0         0         0         0         0
35        8       0         0         0         0         0
36        9       0         0         0         0         0
37       10       0         0         0         0         0
38       11       0         0         0         0         0
39       12       0         0         0         0         0
40
41
42 Amortization Schedule - Effective Interest Method
43                                                          Bond
44               Interest  Cash    Amorti-   (Disc.)  Carrying
45       Year    Expense   Paid    zation    Premium  Value
46       ----    --------  ----    -------   -------  --------
47        0                                  FORMULA14 FORMULA15
48        1 FORMULA16 FORMULA17 FORMULA18 FORMULA19 FORMULA20
49        2 FORMULA21 FORMULA22 FORMULA23 FORMULA24 FORMULA25
```

50	3	0	0	0	0	0
51	4	0	0	0	0	0
52	5	0	0	0	0	0
53	6	0	0	0	0	0
54	7	0	0	0	0	0
55	8	0	0	0	0	0
56	9	0	0	0	0	0
57	10	0	0	0	0	0
58	11	0	0	0	0	0
59	12	0	0	0	0	0

```
60 ----------------------------------------------------------------
61
62
63
64
65
66
67 XXXXXXXXXXXXXXXXXXXXXXXXXXXXXXXXXXXXXXXXXXXXXXXXXXXXXXXXXXXXXXXX
68 Scratch Pad--Display of relevant cash flows
69
70            Annual    Bond
71       Year Interest Maturity
72       ----  --------  --------
73         1   120000          0
74         2   120000          0
75         3   120000          0
76         4   120000          0
77         5   120000          0
78         6   120000          0
79         7   120000          0
80         8   120000          0
81         9   120000          0
82        10   120000    1000000
83        11        0          0
84        12        0          0
```

On May 31, 19X2, P Corporation issued 10,000 shares of its own $5 par common stock for all of S Incorporated's outstanding shares of common stock. The fair market value of the P Corporation stock is $28 per share. The balance sheets of the two companies on May 31, immediately after the acquisition, are as follows:

	P Corp.	S Inc.
Assets		
Cash	$ 54,600	$19,550
Notes receivable	55,000	3,000
Accounts receivable	74,000	37,300
Interest receivable	3,000	0
Inventories	121,300	30,450
Prepaid expenses	11,500	8,400
Investment in S Inc.	280,000	0
Land	62,000	28,000
Buildings and equipment (net)	210,000	130,000
	$871,400	$256,700
	======	======
Liabilities & Stockholders' Equity		
Notes payable	$ 5,000	$40,000
Accounts payable	96,400	44,700
Dividends payable	25,000	0
Interest payable on notes	0	2,000
Common stock, $5 par	325,000	0
Common stock, $ 8 par	0	96,000
Paid in capital in excess of par	250,000	0
Retained earnings	170,000	74,000
	$871,400	$256,700
	======	======

All of S Incorporated's notes payable are owed to P Corporation.

Required

1) You have been asked to prepare a worksheet for a consolidated balance sheet as of May 31. Review the template called CONS that has been provided to assist you. The column totals will change as eliminations are made. The zeros in the consolidated balance sheet column have been preprogrammed, and as formulas are entered on the template these zeros will be replaced by values. Note that there is a row for entering Goodwill on the worksheet. Some textbooks suggest using goodwill, others don't. Use the method shown in your textbook.

2) On the form on the next page, write the elimination entries required to prepare the consolidated balance sheet. Identify each elimination entry by a separate letter (i.e., journal entry a, journal entry b, etc.). Assume that the business combination has been recorded as a purchase. The fair value of S Inc.'s assets correspond to the book carrying amounts, except for land, which is valued at $100,000 for consolidation purposes.

	DATE	DESCRIPTION	POST. REF.	DEBIT	CREDIT	
1						1
2						2
3						3
4						4
5						5
6						6
7						7
8						8
9						9
10						10
11						11
12						12
13						13
14						14
15						15

3) Using the spaces provided below, write the formulas requested in the template. Note that the elimination amounts are to be entered in columns G and I of the worksheet. FORMULA1 has been provided for you as an example.

FORMULA1 ___+D16+E16+G16-I16___   FORMULA4 _____

FORMULA2 _____   FORMULA5 _____

FORMULA3 _____   FORMULA6 _____

4) Load the spreadsheet program and then load the template CONS. Complete the worksheet by entering the formulas and proper eliminations. Also, in columns F and H, enter the letter corresponding to each journal entry you used in Requirement 2 above. Save the completed template as CONS4. Use ALT P to print the template when done. *Check figure: Total consolidated assets (cell J27), $916,100*

What-If Analysis

5) Assume that the company wished to treat the consolidation as a pooling of interests. How would such treatment have affected P Corporation's balance sheet on May 31? S Inc.'s balance sheet? The consolidated balance sheet?

Redo the P Corporation balance sheet assuming that the consolidation had qualified as a pooling of interest. Also, redo the eliminating entries on the worksheet to reflect pooling of interest. Save your answer as CONS5. Use ALT P to print the template when done.

Graphics

6) Retrieve the CONS4 file. Press the F10 key. This is a graphical representation of some of the accounts of P Corp. and S Inc. before and after consolidation. Identify in the spaces provided below the accounts represented by the letters on the X-axis.

A _____

B _____

C _____

D _____

E _____

F _____

TEMPLATE TICKLER

Retrieve the CONS4 template. Assume that when P Corp. issued its 10,000 shares, it only bought 80% of S Inc. Modify the template to include minority interest and redo the elimination entries on the worksheet to reflect this new scenario. Save the completed template as CONST. Print the results when done.

GRAPHICS TICKLER

Retrieve the CONS4 template. Type /Graph, Name, Create, **ORIG**, and press ENTER. Then press **Reset** and **Graph**. Prepare a stacked-bar graph comparing the total cash, notes receivable, and accounts receivable balances of P Corp. with those of S Inc. No graphics data table is needed; use D14.E14 as the X-axis. Enter all appropriate titles, legends, and formatting on the graph. Save the graph as a PIC file called CONSG. Save the template again as CONS4. Print the graph.

MACRO TICKLER

Create a macro named \R on the CONS4 template to print the worksheet itself (range B6.J41) in compressed mode.

Student Name   =
Section Number   =

```
A      B       C       D        E       F      G      H      I        J
```

8   P Corp. & S Inc.
9   Work Sheet for Consolidated Balance Sheet
10   May 31, 19X2

						Eliminations		Consol.
			P Corp.	S Inc.	Debit	Credit		Balance Sheet
16	Cash		$54,600	$19,550				FORMULA1
17	Notes receivable		55,000	3,000				FORMULA2
18	Accounts rec.		74,000	37,300				FORMULA3
19	Interest rec.		3,000	0				0
20	Inventories		121,300	30,450				0
21	Prepaid expenses		11,500	8,400				0
22	Investment in S		280,000	0				0
23	Land		62,000	28,000				0
24	Net build & equip.		210,000	130,000				0
25	Goodwill							0
27	Totals		$871,400	$256,700				$0
30	Notes payable		$5,000	$40,000				FORMULA4
31	Accounts payable		96,400	44,700				FORMULA5
32	Dividends payable		25,000	0				FORMULA6
33	Interest pay/notes		0	2,000				0
34	Common stock, $5		325,000					0
35	Common stock, $8			96,000				0
36	Paid in capital		250,000	0				0
37	Retained earnings		170,000	74,000				0
39	Totals		$871,400	$256,700	$0	$0		$0

The comparative balance sheet of Triple Crown Corporation at April 30, the end of the fiscal year, is as follows:

Triple Crown Corporation
Comparative Balance Sheet
April 30, 19X2 and 19X1

Assets

	19X2	19X1
Cash	$ 38,140	$ 26,400
Accounts receivable	87,500	74,810
Merchandise inventory	133,400	140,620
Prepaid expenses	6,900	7,250
Plant assets	307,000	210,000
Accumulated depreciation--plant assets	(85,700)	(60,000)
Total assets	$487,240	$399,080
	=======	=======

Liabilities & Stockholders' Equity

	19X2	19X1
Accounts payable	$ 40,740	$ 39,480
Dividends payable	36,000	20,000
Bonds payable	80,000	70,000
Common stock, $20 par	160,000	140,000
Premium on common stock	22,000	15,000
Retained earnings	148,500	114,600
Total liabilities & stockholders' equity	$487,240	$399,080
	=======	=======

Additional data obtained from the records of Triple Crown Corporation are as follows:

a. Net income for 19X2 was $69,900.
b. Depreciation reported on income statement for 19X2 was $31,000.
c. Purchased $110,000 of new equipment, putting $60,000 cash down and issuing $50,000 of bonds for the balance.
d. Old equipment originally costing $13,000, with accumulated depreciation of $5,300, was sold for $9,000.
e. Retired $40,000 of bonds.
f. Declared cash dividends of $36,000.
g. Issued 1,000 shares of common stock at $27 cash.

Required

1) You have been asked to prepare a statement of cash flows for Triple Crown Corporation. Review the template called CASH that has been provided to assist you in preparing the statement. The template has been designed so that as you make entries in columns G and I, column J will be automatically updated. Columns F and H are to be used to enter letter references for each of the debit and credit entries on the worksheet.

2) Using the spaces provided below, write the formulas requested in the template. FORMULA1 has been provided for you as an example.

FORMULA1 ___+E17+G17-I17___   FORMULA4 _____

FORMULA2 _____   FORMULA5 _____

FORMULA3 _____   FORMULA6 _____

3) Load the spreadsheet program and then load the template CASH. First, enter the formulas. Then, complete the worksheet in the manner described below:

According to the problem, cash increased from $26,400 to $38,140 during the year. This is a $11,740 increase. To record this increase on the worksheet, move the cursor to row 17. Since this is the first account you are analyzing, enter the letter "a" in column F. Then enter 11740 in column G (a debit since cash increased). This brings the year-end balance (column J) to $38,140, its proper balance.

Now move to the bottom part of the statement where you see the categories Operating Activities, Investing Activities, etc. The credit side of the entry has to be entered here.

The proper space for this cash entry is on row 67. Enter the letter "a" in cell H67 and 11740 in cell I67. Notice the totals at the bottom of the page (row 69) now agree.

The next account balance that changed is accounts receivable. It increased by $12,690. To enter this change on the worksheet, enter the letter "b" in cell F18 and 12690 in cell G18 (again a debit since accounts receivable increased). This brings the year-end balance in column J to $87,500, its proper balance. The change in accounts receivable balance is an operating activity adjustment (as explained in your textbook). Enter the credit side of this entry in cells H39 and I39, and enter the explanation "Increase in accounts receivable" in cell B39.

All other balance sheet accounts must be analyzed in the same manner, placing appropriate debit or credit entries in the top part of the worksheet to obtain the proper balances in column J, and then entering the second side of the entry in the appropriate row on the bottom part of the worksheet. You should use letter references to identify all entries. Also, you must enter a description of the entry in column B under the appropriate activity category. Although a sequence of analyzing the balance sheet from top to bottom is suggested here, this order is not necessary. Your textbook may specify a different sequence. Also, some accounts may have both debit and credit adjustments to them.

The worksheet is not a substitute for a statement of cash flows, but it does provide you with all the numbers you need to properly prepare one.

You will be done with your analysis when

a. The individual account balances at April 30, 19X2 as shown on the template (column J) equal those shown in the problem data above.

b. The transaction column totals are equal (cells G69 and I69).

When you are finished, use ALT P to print the template. Save your completed template as CASH3. *Check figure: Total credits at 4/30/X2 (cell J34) $572,940*

4) On the form on the next page, prepare a statement of cash flows in good form using the indirect method.

What-If Analysis

5) Retrieve the CASH3 template. Suppose that an audit of Triple Crown encountered the following two errors:

a. An accounts receivable totaling $3,000 should have been written off as a bad debt at the end of the year. Year-end accounts receivable should be only $84,500.

b. The $36,000 dividend declared at year-end had in fact been paid. Thus, both the cash account and the dividends payable account are overstated at year-end.

Correct both errors on the worksheet and use ALT P to print your revised template.

6) Retrieve the CASH3 template and press the F10 key. On the graph, the components of cash flow for Triple Crown over the last five years are plotted. Comment below on the behavior of each component. Do you see favorable trends? Unfavorable ones?

_____

_____

_____

_____

TEMPLATE TICKLER

Retrieve the CASH3 template. Prepare the statement of cash flows (see Requirement 4 above). Use columns K through R for your statement. Save the completed template as CASHT. Print the statement when done.

GRAPHICS TICKLER

Retrieve the CASH3 template. Type /Graph, Name, Create ORIG, and press ENTER. Then press Reset and Graph. Prepare a line graph which illustrates the relationship operating cash flows and net income over the last five years. Use the graphics data table in rows 81 through 87 as a basis for preparing the graph. Use all appropriate titles, legends, formatting, etc. Save the graph as a PIC file called CASHG. Save the template again as CASH3. Print the graph.

MACRO TICKLER

Develop a macro named \R on the CASHT template to print the statement of cash flows you prepared for the Template Tickler above.

```
CASH                    Student Name    =
                        Section Number  =
----------------------------------------------------------------------
  A       B       C       D       E    F    G    H    I       J
----------------------------------------------------------------------
  6                      Triple Crown Corporation
  7              Work Sheet for Statement of Cash Flows
  8                   For Year Ended April 30, 19X2
  9  -----------------------------------------------------------------
 10                                        Analysis of
 11                                      Transactions for
 12                              Account  Year Ended 4/30/X2  Account
 13                              Balance  ---------  --------- Balance
 14                              4/30/X1   Debit     Credit   4/30/X2
 15                              -------   -------    -------  -------
 16 Debits
 17    Cash                       26,400                      FORMULA1
 18    Accounts receivable        74,810                      FORMULA2
 19    Merchandise inventory     140,620                      FORMULA3
 20    Prepaid expenses            7,250                             0
 21    Plant assets              210,000                             0
 22                              -------                       -------
 23      Total                   459,080                             0
 24                              =======                       =======
 25 Credits
 26    Accumulated depreciation   60,000                      FORMULA4
 27    Accounts payable           39,480                      FORMULA5
 28    Dividends payable          20,000                      FORMULA6
 29    Bonds payable              70,000                             0
 30    Common stock, $20 par     140,000                             0
 31    Premium on common stock    15,000                             0
 32    Retained earnings         114,600                             0
 33                              -------                       -------
 34      Total                   459,080                             0
 35                              =======                       =======
 36
 37 Operating Activities
 38 --------------------
 39
 40
 41
 42
 43
 44
 45
 46
 47
```

```
48 Investing Activities
49 --------------------
50
51
52
53
54 Financing Activities
55 --------------------
56
57
58
59
60
61 Noncash Investing & Financing
62 -----------------------------
63
64
65                                    -------        -------
66                                       0              0
67 Change in cash
68                                    -------        -------
69                                       0              0
70                                    =======        =======
71 ----------------------------------------------------------------
```

STUDENT NAME _____

SECTION NUMBER _____

The comparative financial statements of Charlie's Shoe Shop are as follows:

Charlie's Shoe Shop
Comparative Income Statement
For Years Ended October 31, 19X9 and 19X8

	19X9	19X8
Net sales	$2,344,050	$2,200,220
Cost of merchandise sold	1,880,000	1,700,000
Gross profit	$ 464,050	$ 500,220
Selling expenses	$ 82,000	$ 85,000
General expenses	54,440	59,000
Total operating expenses	$ 136,440	$ 144,000
Operating income	$ 327,610	$ 356,220
Other expense (interest)	24,000	13,000
Income before income tax	$ 303,610	$ 343,220
Income tax	109,600	147,270
Net income	$ 194,010	$ 195,950

Charlie's Shoe Shop
Comparative Retained Earnings Statement
For Years Ended October 31, 19X9 and 19X8

	19X9	19X8
Retained earnings, November 1	$ 946,730	$ 790,780
Net income for year	194,010	195,950
Total	$1,140,740	$ 986,730
Common stock dividends	55,000	40,000
Retained earnings, October 31	$1,085,740	$ 946,730

Charlie's Shoe Shop
Comparative Balance Sheet
October 31, 19X9 and 19X8

	19X9	19X8
Assets		
Cash	$ 23,220	$ 42,000
Accounts receivable	155,000	199,050
Merchandise inventory	550,320	425,000
Prepaid expenses	15,000	17,000
Plant assets (net)	1,200,000	1,020,000
Total assets	$1,943,540	$1,703,050

Liabilities & Stockholders' Equity		
Accounts payable	$ 217,600	$ 226,120
Bonds payable, 10% due 19X2	240,000	130,000
Total liabilities	$ 457,600	$ 356,120
Common stock	$ 400,200	$ 400,200
Retained earnings	1,085,740	946,730
Total stockholders' equity	$1,485,940	$1,346,930
Total liabilities & stockholders' equity	$1,943,540	$1,703,050
	=======	=======

Required

1) Review the template RATIO that follows these requirements. You have been asked to perform a ratio analysis of this company for 19X9.

2) In the spaces provided below, write the formulas requested.

FORMULA1 _____   FORMULA6 _____

FORMULA2 _____   FORMULA7 _____

FORMULA3 _____   FORMULA8 _____

FORMULA4 _____   FORMULA9 _____

FORMULA5 _____   FORMULA10 _____

3) Load the spreadsheet program and then load the template RATIO. Enter the formulas in the appropriate cells. Save the completed model as RATIO3. Use ALT P to print the template when done. *Check figure: Acid test (quick) ratio (cell H80), .82*

4) a. What information does a comparison of the current ratio and acid-test ratio provide?

_____

_____

_____

b. Is the company using leverage to its advantage? Explain.

_____

_____

_____

c. What other observations can be made comparing Charlie's ratios to the following industry norms:

Acid test ratio	1.0
Current ratio	2.0
Accounts receivable turnover	12.0
Inventory turnover	4.0
Gross profit ratio	40%
Net income to sales	7%
Rate earned on total assets	12%
Rate earned on common stock equity	20%
Debt to total assets	.35
Times interest earned	8

_____

_____

_____

_____

_____

_____

What-If Analysis

5) With your completed template still on the screen, you will now combine it with another template called RATIO5 from your Template Disk. This file contains financial data for Charlie's for the next year (19X0). The combining process was not discussed in the tutorial, so follow these instructions carefully. To begin, position the cursor in cell A1, type /FCCE RATIO5, and press ENTER. This procedure copies the data from the file RATIO5 into the file on the screen (RATIO3). Note that the Data Section on this template now contains information for 19X0 and 19X9. Your formulas will automatically recalculate the ratios with the new data. Use ALT P to print the template. Save the new file as RATIONEW.

6) Compare your printout from Requirement 3 with your printout from Requirement 5. From these two sets of ratios, what conclusions can be drawn concerning changes from 19X9 and 19X0?

_____

_____

_____

_____

_____

_____

Graphics

7) With the 19X0 data still on the screen, press the F10 key. The graph presented shows the rates of return for Charlie's Shoe Shop for the last five years. Answer the following questions:

a. In 19X6, the rate of return on assets exceeded the rate of return on common stockholders' equity. Why might this have occurred? Be as specific as possible.

_____

_____

_____

_____

b. Is the company better off in 19X0 than it was in 19X6? Why or why not?

_____

_____

_____

_____

TEMPLATE TICKLER

Retrieve the RATIONEW template. Modify the template to have it compute two additional activity ratios: number of days' sales in receivables and number of days' sales in merchandise inventory. Use the 19X9 and 19X0 data and assume a 365-day year. Print the results when done. Write out the formulas for your ratios below.

Days' sales in receivables _____

Days' sales in inventory _____

Save the completed template as RATIOT.

GRAPHICS TICKLER

Retrieve the RATIONEW template. Type /Graph, Name, Create, **ORIG**, and press ENTER. Then press Reset and Graph. Prepare a bar graph which compares the acid-test and current ratios for Charlie's Shoe Shop for 19X9 and 19X0. Use the graphics data table in rows 101 to 103 as a basis for preparing the graph. Enter all appropriate titles, legends, and formats. Save the graph as a PIC file called RATIOG. Save the template again as RATIONEW. Print the graph.

MACRO TICKLER

Develop a macro named \R on the RATIO3 template to automatically execute the file combine steps from Requirement 5.

Student Name   =
Section Number =

A   B   C   D   E   F   G   H

---

6 Data Section:

7   Charlie's Shoe Shop
8   Comparative Income Statement
9   For Years Ended October 31, 19X9 and 19X8

10 ---

						19X9	19X8
11						19X9	19X8
12						----	----
13 Net sales						$2,344,050	$2,200,220
14 Cost of merchandise sold						1,880,000	1,700,000
15						----------	----------
16 Gross profit						$464,050	$500,220
17						----------	----------
18 Selling expenses						$82,000	$85,000
19 General expenses						54,440	59,000
20						----------	----------
21 Total operating expenses						$136,440	$144,000
22						----------	----------
23 Operating income						$327,610	$356,220
24 Other expenses (interest)						24,000	13,000
25						----------	----------
26 Income before income tax						$303,610	$343,220
27 Income tax						109,600	147,270
28						----------	----------
29 Net income						$194,010	$195,950
30						==========	==========

31

32   Charlie's Shoe Shop
33   Comparative Retained Earnings Statement
34   For Years Ended October 31, 19X9 and 19X8

35 ---

						19X9	19X8
36						19X9	19X8
37						----	----
38 Retained earnings, November 1						$946,730	$790,780
39 Net income for year						194,010	195,950
40						----------	----------
41 Total						$1,140,740	$986,730
42 Common stock dividends						55,000	40,000
43						----------	----------
44 Retained earnings, October 31						$1,085,740	$946,730
45						==========	==========

46

```
47                    Charlie's Shoe Shop
48                 Comparative Balance Sheet
49              As of October 31, 19X9 and 19X8
50 ------------------------------------------------------------
51                                        19X9         19X8
52                  Assets                ----         ----
53 Cash                                 $23,220      $42,000
54 Accounts receivable                  155,000      199,050
55 Merchandise inventory                550,320      425,000
56 Prepaid expenses                      15,000       17,000
57 Plant assets (net)                 1,200,000    1,020,000
58                                   ----------   ----------
59 Total assets                     $1,943,540   $1,703,050
60                                   ==========   ==========
61
62        Liabilities & Stockholders' Equity
63 Accounts payable                    $217,600     $226,120
64 Bonds payable, 10% due 19X2          240,000      130,000
65                                   ----------   ----------
66 Total liabilities                   $457,600     $356,120
67                                   ----------   ----------
68 Common stock                        $400,200     $400,200
69 Retained earnings                  1,085,740      946,730
70                                   ----------   ----------
71 Total stockholders' equity       $1,485,940   $1,346,930
72                                   ----------   ----------
73 Total liabilities & stockholders' equity  $1,943,540 $1,703,050
74                                   ==========   ==========
75
76 ------------------------------------------------------------
77 Answer Section:
78
79 Liquidity ratios:
80      Acid-test (quick) ratio                  FORMULA1
81      Current ratio                            FORMULA2
82 Activity ratios:
83      Accounts receivable turnover             FORMULA3
84      Inventory turnover                       FORMULA4
85 Profitability ratios:
86      Gross profit ratio                       FORMULA5
87      Net income to sales                      FORMULA6
88      Rate earned on total assets              FORMULA7
89      Rate earned on common stock equity       FORMULA8
90 Coverage ratios:
91      Debt to total assets                     FORMULA9
92      Times interest earned                    FORMULA10
93 ------------------------------------------------------------
```

P17 MANUFACTURING ACCOUNTING (MFG)

STUDENT NAME _____

SECTION NUMBER _____

The following information is for Osborne Tool and Die for the year ended December 31, 19X8:

Depreciation--equipment	$ 30,000
Direct labor	428,000
Direct materials inventory, 1/1/X8	61,000
Direct materials inventory, 12/31/X8	62,000
Factory rent	50,940
Finished goods, 1/1/X8	88,000
Finished goods, 12/31/X8	115,000
Indirect labor	25,000
Indirect materials	17,500
Purchases of direct materials	430,120
Work in process, 1/1/X8	20,200
Work in process, 12/31/X8	19,110

Required

1) You have been asked to prepare a schedule of cost of goods manufactured and sold for the year just ended. Review the template MFG that follows these requirements.

2) Using the spaces provided below, write the formulas and titles where requested.

FORMULA1 _____   FORMULA7 _____

FORMULA2 _____   FORMULA8 _____

FORMULA3 _____   FORMULA9 _____

FORMULA4 _____   FORMULA10 _____

FORMULA5 _____   FORMULA11 _____

FORMULA6 _____   FORMULA12 _____

TITLE A _____   TITLE E _____

TITLE B _____   TITLE F _____

TITLE C _____   TITLE G _____

TITLE D _____   TITLE H _____

3) Load the spreadsheet program and then load the template MFG. Enter the formulas and titles where requested on the template. The cells that contain zeros now will change to non-zero values as formulas are entered. Use ALT P to print the template. Save the model as MFG3. *Check figure: Cost of goods sold (cell H55), $954,650*

What-If Analysis

4) The following data pertains to 19X9 activities of Osborne Tool and Die:

Depreciation--equipment	$ 31,000
Direct labor	443,000
Direct materials inventory, 12/31/X9	56,700
Factory rent	54,000
Finished goods, 12/31/X9	121,000
Indirect labor	28,000
Indirect materials	20,000
Purchases of direct materials	402,200
Work in process, 12/31/X9	18,150

Use your completed template to determine the firm's cost of goods sold for 19X9. Remember to change the year in cell G26. Use ALT P to print your answer. Save the 19X9 template as MFG4.

If sales and other expenses were identical in 19X8 and 19X9, during which year did Osborne earn more income? Why?

_____

_____

_____

_____

Graphics

5) Retrieve MFG3 and press the F10 key. The management of Osborne is convinced that the quality of their products is highly dependent on their relative labor costs. Experience has shown that direct labor should account for at least 45% of the total product cost. From the pie graph that appears on the screen, Osborne did not achieve this goal in 19X8. How much should Osborne have spent on direct labor to reach its 45% goal?

To find out, try different values for direct labor (cell G9), pressing the ENTER and F10 keys after each attempt. When you find a direct labor level that increases the direct labor percentage to 45%, enter the answer below:

In 19X8, direct labor needed to be $_____

Retrieve MFG4 and press the F10 key. Did Osborne achieve its 45% goal in 19X9? If not, answer the following:

In 19X9, direct labor needed to be $_____

TEMPLATE TICKLER

Retrieve the MFG3 template. This template presents the company's manufacturing activities for 19X8. The company also had the following selling and general activities in 19X8: sales of $2,250,500, selling expenses of $400,000, and general expenses of $200,000. Modify the template to include this information in the Data Section and change the Answer Section so that it is in the form of an income statement. Print the template when done.

Hint: Expand the Data Section to include these additional input items alphabetically. Widen column G. Insert a row for sales under the heading in the Answer Section. Add the rest of the income statement information to the bottom of the schedule. You will need to enter formulas for gross profit, all the expenses, and net income. You will also need to change the statement name. Save the completed template as MFGT. Print the template when done.

GRAPHICS TICKLER

Retrieve the MFG4 template. Type /Graph, Name, Create, **ORIG**, and press ENTER. Then press **Reset** and **Graph**. Prepare a stacked-bar graph to show the dollar amount of materials, labor, and overhead incurred by Osborne in 19X8 and 19X9. Complete the graphics data table in rows 71 to 75 as a basis for preparing the graph. Use your print-out to add the 19X8 data in column C. Use C72.D72 as the X-axis. Enter all appropriate titles, legends, and formats. Save the graph as a PIC file called MFGG. Save the template again as MFG3. Print the graph.

MACRO TICKLER

Create a macro named **\R** on the MFG3 template to print the Answer Section before the Data Section.

| MFG | | | | Student Name | = | | | |
| | | | | Section Number | = | | | |

A	B	C	D	E	F	G	H
6 Data Section:							
7							
8 Depreciation--equipment						$30,000	
9 Direct labor						428,000	
10 Direct materials inventory, 1/1						61,000	
11 Direct materials inventory, 12/31						62,000	
12 Factory rent						50,940	
13 Finished goods, 1/1						88,000	
14 Finished goods, 12/31						115,000	
15 Indirect labor						25,000	
16 Indirect materials						17,500	
17 Purchases of direct materials						430,120	
18 Work in process, 1/1						20,200	
19 Work in process, 12/31						19,110	
20							
21							

```
22 Answer Section:
23
24                      Osborne Tool and Die
25          Schedule of Cost of Goods Manufactured and Sold
26              For the Year Ended December 31, 19X8
27 -----------------------------------------------------------------
28 Direct materials
29   Direct materials inventory, 1/1                    $61,000
30   Add:    TITLE A                                    FORMULA1
31                                                      ----------
32   Cost of direct materials available                     $0
33   Less:   TITLE B                                    FORMULA2
34                                                      ----------
35 Cost of direct materials used                        FORMULA3
36 Direct labor                                         428,000
37 Manufacturing overhead:
38   Factory rent                          $50,940
39   TITLE C                               FORMULA4
40   TITLE D                               FORMULA5
41   TITLE E                               FORMULA6           0
42                                         ------- ----------
43 Total manufacturing costs                            FORMULA7
44   Work in process, 1/1                                20,200
45                                                      ----------
46   Total work in process available                        $0
47   Less:  TITLE F                                     FORMULA8
48                                                      ----------
49 Cost of goods manufactured                           FORMULA9
50   TITLE G                                            FORMULA10
51                                                      ----------
52   Cost of goods available for sale                   FORMULA11
53   Less:    Finished goods, 12/31                     115,000
54                                                      ----------
55 TITLE H                                              FORMULA12
56                                                      ==========
57 -----------------------------------------------------------------
```

142

P18 PROCESS COSTING
(PROCESS)

STUDENT NAME _____

SECTION NUMBER _____

The following information is provided for Prater Dynamics, Inc. for the month of April. All materials are added to production at the beginning of the manufacturing process, and conversion costs are incurred uniformly throughout manufacturing. Prater uses the FIFO inventory method.

	Units	Cost
Work in process, 4/1/X7 (30% completed)	40,000	$ 63,200
Materials added during April		100,000
Conversion costs incurred during April		400,000
Units completed during April	140,000	
Work in process, 4/30/X7 (60% completed)	20,000	

Required

1) You have been asked to prepare a cost of production report for the month of April. The template PROCESS contains all of the problem data in the Data Section and a partially completed cost of production report in the Answer Section. Study the Answer Section carefully to make sure that you understand the five-step format used by Prater for its cost of production report. (Production cost report formats vary a great deal from company to company.)

2) Using the spaces provided below, write the 16 formulas requested. FORMULA3 has been done for you as an example.

FORMULA1 _____   FORMULA9 _____

FORMULA2 _____   FORMULA10 _____

FORMULA3 ____+F11*(1-E11)____   FORMULA11 _____

FORMULA4 _____   FORMULA12 _____

FORMULA5 _____   FORMULA13 _____

FORMULA6 _____   FORMULA14 _____

FORMULA7 _____   FORMULA15 _____

FORMULA8 _____   FORMULA16 _____

3) Load the spreadsheet program and then load the template PROCESS. Enter the formulas where indicated on the template. Use ALT P to print the template. Save your completed model as PROCESS3. *Check figure: Materials cost per equivalent unit (cell G63), $.83*

What-If Analysis

4) Test your template with the following data for the month of May. Use ALT P to print the results when done. Save your results as PROCESS4.

	Units	Cost
Work in process, 5/1/X7 (60% completed)	20,000	$ 50,952
Materials added during May		108,000
Conversion costs incurred during May		288,000
Units completed during May	115,000	
Work in process, 5/31/X7 (10% completed)	25,000	

5) On the form below, record the journal entry to transfer the completed goods from work in process to finished goods for the month of May.

JOURNAL   PAGE

	DATE		DESCRIPTION	POST. REF.	DEBIT	CREDIT	
1							1
2							2
3							3
4							4
5							5

Graphics

6) The owners of Prater Dynamics keep very close tabs on their manufacturing costs. Assuming the quality of the product is unchanged from April to May, in which month is cost efficiency the best? To find out, retrieve PROCESS4 and press the F10 key. Review the graph and write your conclusions below. Verify your observations by reference to the printouts of PROCESS3 and PROCESS4.

_____

_____

_____

_____

_____

_____

_____

TEMPLATE TICKLER

Retrieve the PROCESS3 template. Revise the template to put the Answer Section on top and the Data Section at the bottom. Save the completed template as PROCESST. Print the results.

GRAPHICS TICKLER

Retrieve the PROCESS3 template. Type /Graph, Name, Create, **ORIG**, and press ENTER. Then press **Reset** and **Graph**. Prepare a pie graph which discloses the relative proportion of materials and conversion costs per equivalent unit in April. No graphics data table is needed; use G61.H61 as the X-axis and G63.H63 as the A-range. Enter all appropriate titles, legends, and formats. Save the graph as a PIC file called PROCESSG. Save the template again as PROCESS3. Print the graph.

MACRO TICKLER

Create a macro named **\R** on the PROCESS3 template to automatically complete the Template Tickler.

144

```
PROCESS                 Student Name   =
                        Section Number =
------------------------------------------------------------------
A       B       C       D       E       F       G       H
------------------------------------------------------------------
 6 Data Section:
 7
 8                                      Percent
 9                              Completed  Units     Cost
10                              ---------  -----     ----
11 Work in process, beginning       30%   40,000   $63,200
12 Materials added                                  100,000
13 Conversion costs incurred                        400,000
14 Units completed during month           140,000
15 Work in process, ending          60%   20,000
16
17 -----------------------------------------------------------
18 Answer Section:
19                      Prater Dynamics, Inc.
20                   Cost of Production Report
21                     For Month of April 19X7
22 -----------------------------------------------------------
23 1) Units to account for:
24
25 Beg. work in proc.   40,000       Units completed     140,000
26 Units started       FORMULA1      End. work in proc.   20,000
27                      -------                           -------
28 Total units to be                 Total units
29 accounted for             0       Accounted for       160,000
30                      =======                           =======
31
32 -----------------------------------------------------------
33 2) Costs to account for:
34                                      Total
35                                      --------
36 Beginning work in process           $63,200
37 Materials added                      100,000
38 Conversion costs incurred            400,000
39                                      --------
40          Total costs                $563,200
41                                      ========
42
43 -----------------------------------------------------------
```

```
44 3) Equivalent unit computations:
45                                                     Equivalent units
46                                          Total   ------------------
47                                          Units Materials Conver.
48                                          -------- -------- --------
49 Beginning work in process               40,000 FORMULA2 FORMULA3
50 Units started and completed             FORMULA4 FORMULA5 FORMULA6
51 Ending work in process                  20,000 FORMULA7 FORMULA8
52                                          -------- -------- --------
53          Total units *                       0
54                                          ========
55          Total equivalent units                      0        0
56                                                  ======== ========
57 * Total must agree with step 1.
58
59 ------------------------------------------------------------
60 4) Costs per equivalent unit:
61    (Rounded to nearest cent)                   Materials Conver.
62                                                 -------- --------
63                                                 FORMULA9 FORMULA10
64
65
66    Total unit cost (materials + conversion)      = FORMULA11
67
68 ------------------------------------------------------------
69 5) Production cost allocation:
70
71 Beginning work in process:
72    Prior period cost                      FORMULA12
73    Conversion of beginning work in process FORMULA13        $0
74                                            --------
75 Units started and completed                             FORMULA14
76 Ending work in process:
77    Materials                              FORMULA15
78    Conversion                             FORMULA16
79                                            --------
80       Total ending work in process                         0
81                                                         --------
82 Total costs accounted for *                               $0
83                                                         ========
84 * Total must agree with step 2.
85
86 ------------------------------------------------------------
```

P19 COST-VOLUME-PROFIT ANALYSIS (CVP)

STUDENT NAME _____

SECTION NUMBER _____

Dallas Manufacturing maintains the same level of inventory at the end of each year. It has provided the following information about expenses anticipated for 19X6, when it expects to sell 110,000 units of its product for $16 each:

	Fixed Expenses	Variable Expenses (per unit sold)
Production costs:		
Direct materials		$ 2.70
Direct labor		4.30
Factory overhead	$300,000	2.00
Selling expenses:		
Sales salaries and commissions	78,000	.80
Advertising	57,500	
Miscellaneous selling expenses	14,300	
General expenses:		
Office salaries	96,000	
Supplies	17,200	.20
Miscellaneous general expense	10,000	
	$573,000	$10.00

Required

1) The president of Dallas has asked you to calculate the company's break-even point in dollars and in units for 19X6. Also, compute Dallas' contribution margin per unit, contribution margin ratio, and projected net income for 19X6. The template CVP has been provided to assist you. Note that the data from the problem have already been entered into the Data Section of the worksheet.

2) In the spaces provided below, write the five formulas requested in the template.

FORMULA1 _____   FORMULA4 _____

FORMULA2 _____   FORMULA5 _____

FORMULA3 _____

3) Load the spreadsheet program and load the template CVP. Enter the formulas where indicated on the template. Save the solution as CVP3 and use ALT P to print the results. *Check figure: Dollar sales at break-even point (cell G33), $1,528,000*

What-If Analysis

4) The president of Dallas would like to know the effect that the following suggestions for improving performance would have on unit sales needed to break-even and on projected net income for 19X6. Each change should be considered independently by retrieving CVP3 before each change. Write the unit sales needed in the blanks below.

   a. Put all sales personnel on commission. This would eliminate the $78,000 fixed sales salaries expense; variable sales commissions would increase to $2.00 per unit. This would increase unit sales by 20,000 units.

b. Redesign the package for the product. This will cut $.40 from the variable cost of the product (direct materials) but will increase fixed factory overhead by $5,000 for additional depreciation on the new packaging machine.

c. Undertake a new advertising campaign on cable TV. This would cost $30,000 more than is currently planned for advertising but would be expected to increase sales volume by 4,000 units.

d. Cut the price of the product by $1. This should increase sales volume by 20,000 units.

UNITS NEEDED TO MEET

		Break-even Point	Projected Net Income
Original data		_____	_____
	a.	_____	_____
	b.	_____	_____
	c.	_____	_____
	d.	_____	_____

5) From the analysis above, should Dallas use any of the suggestions?

_____

_____

_____

_____

_____

_____

_____

_____

Graphics

6) Retrieve the CVP3 template. Press the F10 key. On the screen, you will see a Cost-Volume-Profit graph (also commonly called a Break-Even Chart). In the space provided below, identify the names of the data ranges.

Data Range Represented By:

(square) _____

(diamond) _____

(triangle) _____

Use the graph to answer the following questions:

a. What is the break-even point (approximately) in units? _____

b. What is the approximate profit or loss if Dallas sells 40,000 units?_____

c. What dollar amount of fixed factory overhead would push the break-even point to 120,000 units? (Hint: Enter different amounts in cell F11 and press the F10 key until the desired result is achieved).

---

d. Reset cell F11 to its original value of $300,000. What selling price would push the break-even point to 80,000 units?

TEMPLATE TICKLER

Retrieve the CVP3 template. The president of the company would like to have the template display an income statement in a contribution margin format (Sales - variable costs = contribution margin - fixed costs = net income). Begin the statement on line 37 of the template. Save the completed template as CVPT. Print the results.

GRAPHICS TICKLER

Retrieve the CVP3 template. Type /Graph, Name, Create, ORIG, and press ENTER. Then press Reset and Graph. Create a line graph in which profit or loss is plotted on the Y-axis and sales volume is plotted on the X-axis. Sales volume can be expressed in either units or dollars. Use units for your graph. Revise the graphics data table in rows 83 through 87 to include a column for profits. Use this table as a basis for preparing the graph. Enter appropriate titles, legends, and formats. Save the graph as a PIC file called CVPG. Save the template again as CVP3. Print the graph.

MACRO TICKLER

Develop a macro named \R on the CVP3 template to automatically reset the Data Section to its original values. This could be used to get the template back to its original state after trying each "what-if" scenario.

```
CVP                    Student Name      =
                       Section Number    =
------------------------------------------------------------------
A      B        C        D        E           F           G
------------------------------------------------------------------
 6 Data Section:                            Fixed       Variable
 7                                          -----       --------
 8 Production costs:
 9   Direct materials                                    $2.70
10   Direct labor                                         4.30
11   Factory overhead                     $300,000        2.00
12 Selling expenses:
13   Sales salaries & commissions           78,000         .80
14   Advertising                            57,500
15   Miscellaneous selling expense          14,300
16 General expenses:
17   Office salaries                        96,000
18   Supplies                               17,200         .20
19   Miscellaneous general expense          10,000
20                                         --------      ------
21                                         $573,000      $10.00
22                                         ========      ======
23
24 Selling price per unit           $16.00
25 Expected unit sales             110,000
26
27 ------------------------------------------------------------------
28 Answer Section:
29
30 Contribution margin per unit                      FORMULA1
31 Contribution margin ratio                         FORMULA2
32 Unit sales at break-even point                    FORMULA3
33 Dollar sales at break-even point                  FORMULA4
34 Expected net income                               FORMULA5
35 ------------------------------------------------------------------
```

150

P20 VARIABLE COSTING (VARCOST)

STUDENT NAME _____

SECTION NUMBER _____

The records of Zander Industrial contain the following information for the month of February:

Actual production in units	80,000
Sales in units	60,000
Sales price per unit	$ 20
Variable manufacturing cost per unit	9
Variable selling expense per unit	1
Fixed manufacturing cost	420,000
Fixed selling expenses	65,000

The company has no beginning inventory.

Required

1) As Zander's accountant, you have been asked to prepare a variable costing (direct costing) income statement and an absorption costing income statement for the month of February. Review template VARCOST that follows these requirements.

2) Using the spaces provided below, write the 10 formulas requested. FORMULA1 has been written for you as an example.

FORMULA1 _____+G9*G10_____   FORMULA6 _____

FORMULA2 _____   FORMULA7 _____

FORMULA3 _____   FORMULA8 _____

FORMULA4 _____   FORMULA9 _____

FORMULA5 _____   FORMULA10 _____

3) Load the spreadsheet program and then load the template VARCOST. Enter the formulas where indicated on the template. Use ALT P to print the template. Save the completed model as VARCOST3. *Check figure: Absorption income (cell G35), $220,000*

4) In the space below, explain why the operating income calculated by the absorption method is not the same as that calculated by the variable cost method.

_____

_____

_____

_____

_____

What-If Analysis

5) To determine the effect of different levels of production on the company's income, move the cursor to cell G8 (Actual Production). Change the number in G8 to the different production levels given in the table

below. The first level, 80,000 is the current level. What happens to operating income on both statements as production levels change? Enter the operating incomes in the table below.

February Operating Income	Production Level		
	80,000	70,000	60,000
Absorption	$_____	$_____	$_____
Variable	$_____	$_____	$_____

Does the level of production affect income under either costing method? Explain your findings.

_____

_____

_____

_____

Graphics

6) Retrieve VARCOST3. Press the F10 key. This graph is based on the problem data and the two income statements. Answer the following questions about the graph:

a. What is the title for the X-axis? _____

_____

b. What is the title for the Y-axis? _____

_____

c. What does the first data range (the squares) represent? _____

_____

d. What does the second data range (the crosses) represent? _____

_____

e. Why do the two data ranges cross?_____

_____

f. What would be a good title for this graph? _____

_____

TEMPLATE TICKLER

Retrieve the VARCOST3 template. This template is capable of calculating variable and absorption income when unit sales are equal to or less than production. An equally common situation (that this template cannot handle) is when beginning inventory is present and sales volume exceeds production volume. Revise the template Data Section to include:

Beginning inventory in units	15,000
Beginning inventory cost (absorption)	$213,750
Beginning inventory cost (variable)	$135,000

Also, change actual production (cell G8) to 50,000.

Revise the Answer Section to accommodate this new data. Assume that Zander uses the weighted average costing method for inventory. *Check figure: absorption income, $74,615*

GRAPHICS TICKLER

Retrieve the VARCOST3 template. Do not reset the graph. However, type /Graph, Name, Create, ORIG, and press ENTER to name the original graph. Fix up the graph used in Requirement 6 by adding appropriate titles and legends and formatting the X- and Y-axes. Save the graph as a PIC file called VARCOSTG. Save the template again as VARCOST3. Print the graph.

MACRO TICKLER

Create two macros on the VARCOST3 template, one of which (\A) prints only the absorption income statement and the other (\V) prints only the variable income statement.

```
VARCOST                    Student Name   =
                           Section Number =
---------------------------------------------------------------------
A       B         C         D         E       F        G         H
---------------------------------------------------------------------
 6 Data Section:
 7
 8 Actual production in units                          80,000
 9 Sales in units                                      60,000
10 Sales price per unit                                   $20
11 Variable manufacturing costs per unit                  $9
12 Variable selling costs per unit                        $1
13 Fixed manufacturing costs               $420,000
14 Fixed selling expenses                   $65,000
15
16 --------------------------------------------------------------------
```

```
17 Answer Section:
18
19 Income statement: Absorption costing
20
21 Sales                                    FORMULA1
22 Cost of goods sold:
23    Variable manufacturing costs          FORMULA2
24    Fixed manufacturing costs             FORMULA3
25                                         ----------
26    Total goods available for sale              $0
27    Less ending inventory                 FORMULA4
28                                         ----------
29      Cost of goods sold                        $0
30                                         ----------
31 Gross profit                                   $0
32 Fixed selling expenses                   FORMULA5
33 Variable selling expenses                FORMULA6
34                                         ----------
35 Operating income                               $0
36                                         ==========
37 _____
38
39 Income statement: Variable costing
40
41 Sales                                          $0
42 Cost of goods sold:
43    Variable manufacturing costs          FORMULA7
44    Less ending inventory                 FORMULA8
45                                         ----------
46      Variable cost of goods sold               $0
47                                         ----------
48 Manufacturing margin                           $0
49 Variable selling expenses                FORMULA9
50                                         ----------
51 Contribution margin                            $0
52 Fixed manufacturing costs                FORMULA10
53 Fixed selling expenses                          0
54                                         ----------
55 Operating income                               $0
56                                         ==========
57 ----------------------------------------------------------
```

154

STUDENT NAME _____

SECTION NUMBER _____

Viking Telebike, a mail order bicycle company, has provided the following information at May 31, 19X5:

Units Sales, 19X5

April	1,500	actual
May	1,000	actual
June	1,600	budgeted
July	1,400	budgeted
August	1,500	budgeted
September	1,200	budgeted

Balance Sheet, May 31, 19X5

Cash	$ 8,000
Accounts receivable	107,800
Merchandise inventory	52,800
Fixed assets (net)	130,000
Total assets	$298,600
	======
Accounts payable (merchandise)	$ 74,800
Owner's equity	223,800
Total liabilities and equity	$298,600
	======

Other information:

Average selling price, $98
Average purchase price per unit, $55
Desired ending inventory, 60% of next month's unit sales
Collections from customers:

In month of sale	20%
In month after sale	60%
Two months after sale	20%

Projected cash payments:

Inventory purchases are paid for in month following acquisition.
Variable cash expenses, other than inventory, are equal to 30% of each month's sales and are paid in month of sale.
Fixed cash expenses are $10,000 per month and are paid in month incurred.
Depreciation on equipment is $1,000 per month.

Required

1) As accountant for the company, you have been asked to prepare a master budget for the upcoming quarter (June, July, and August). The components of this budget are a monthly sales budget, a monthly purchases budget, a monthly cash budget, a forecasted income statement for the quarter, and a forecasted August 31 balance sheet. The template MASTER has been provided to assist you.

Viking desires to maintain a cash balance of $8,000 at the end of each month. If this goal cannot be met, the company borrows the exact amount needed to reach its goal. If the company has a cash balance greater than $8,000 and loans payable outstanding, the amount of excess of $8,000 is paid to the bank. Annual interest of 18% is paid on a monthly basis on the outstanding balance.

2) In the spaces provided below, write the formulas requested on the template. FORMULA1 has been provided for you as an example.

FORMULA1 _____+F11_____   FORMULA15 _____

FORMULA2 _____   FORMULA16 _____

FORMULA3 _____   FORMULA17 _____

FORMULA4 _____   FORMULA18 _____

FORMULA5 _____   FORMULA19 _____

FORMULA6 _____   FORMULA20 _____

FORMULA7 _____   FORMULA21 _____

FORMULA8 _____   FORMULA22 _____

FORMULA9 _____   FORMULA23 _____

FORMULA10 _____   FORMULA24 _____

FORMULA11 _____   FORMULA25 _____

FORMULA12 _____   FORMULA26 _____

FORMULA13 _____   FORMULA27 _____

FORMULA14 _____   FORMULA28 _____

3) Load the spreadsheet program and then load the template MASTER. Enter all the formulas where indicated on the template. Check to be sure that your balance sheet balances. Use ALT P to print the template. Save the completed file as MASTER3. *Check figures: Forecasted net income (cell H119), $27,957; total assets (cell H131), $324,357*

4) Review the completed master budget and answer the following questions:

a. Is Viking Telebike expecting to earn a profit during the next quarter? If so, how much?

_____

b. Does the company need to borrow cash during the quarter? Can it make any repayments? Explain.

_____

_____

c. Calculate the debt ratio (total liabilities divided by total assets) for Viking.

_____

_____

What-If Analysis

5) Suppose the company has to revise its estimates because of a downturn in the economy. Unit sales for July, August, and September will be half (50%) of the original estimates. Revise the estimates in cells F12

through F14. After this is done, check your forecasted balance sheet. It should still balance! What effect will this new state of affairs have on net income, cash flow, and debt ratio? Explain why these items changed.

_____

_____

_____

_____

_____

_____

6) Suppose the company has just the opposite news and now expects unit sales for July, August, and September to be double (200%) the original estimates. What effect will this have on the company's net income, cash flow, and debt ratio? Explain your findings.

_____

_____

_____

_____

_____

_____

_____

_____

_____

Graphics

7) Retrieve the MASTER3 template. Press the F10 key. You will see a chart plotting sales and net income over a range of sales volumes (100% equals the original problem data). This is a graphical representation of the sales and net income components of Requirements 5 and 6. A review of this graph raises two additional questions about the relationship between sales and net income:

a. From the graph, estimate sales volumes (roughly), in percentage and dollars, that are required for Viking to break-even (net income equals $0) during this quarter.

Expected volume percent _____%

Sales (dollars) $_____

b. Notice that net income is rising slower than sales volume? Is this a problem?

_____

_____

_____

_____

_____

TEMPLATE TICKLER

Retrieve the MASTER3 template. Viking wants to have each budget not only show monthly figures but also totals for the quarter. Use column I to present totals for all budget lines (except in the budgeted income statement and balance sheet). Consult your textbook for proper treatment of beginning and ending balances in the production, purchases, and cash budgets. Save your completed template as MASTERT. Use the compressed mode to print the template when done.

GRAPHICS TICKLER

Retrieve the MASTER3 template. Type /Graph, Name, Create, **ORIG**, and press ENTER. Then press **Reset** and **Graph**. Create a line graph to show the monthly sales volume in units, from April through September. No graphics data table is needed; use F9.F14 as the A-range. Save the graph as a PIC file called MASTERG. Save the template again as MASTER3. Print the graph.

MACRO TICKLER

Develop a print macro named \R on the MASTER3 template which will print the sales and purchases budgets on page 1, the cash budget on page 2, the income statement on page 3, and the balance sheet on page 4.

```
MASTER                  Student Name   =
                        Section Number =
--------------------------------------------------------------------
 A      B       C       D       E       F       G       H
--------------------------------------------------------------------
 6 Data Section:
 7
 8 Actual and Budgeted Unit Sales:
 9                      April                   1,500
10                      May                     1,000
11                      June                    1,600
12                      July                    1,400
13                      August                  1,500
14                      September               1,200
15
16 Balance Sheet, May 31, 19X5
17      Cash                            $8,000
18      Accounts receivable             107,800
19      Merchandise inventory            52,800
20      Fixed assets (net)              130,000
21                                      --------
22          Total assets               $298,600
23                                      ========
24      Accounts payable (merchandise)  $74,800
25      Owner's equity                  223,800
26                                      --------
27          Total liabilities & equity $298,600
28                                      ========
29
```

```
30 Average selling price                        $98
31 Average purchase cost per unit               $55
32 Desired ending inventory
33    (% of next month's unit sales)            60%
34 Collections from customers:
35    Collected in month of sale                20%
36    Collected in month after sale             60%
37    Collected two months after sale           20%
38 Projected cash payments:
39    Variable expenses                          30% of sales
40    Fixed expenses (per month)        $10,000
41 Depreciation per month               $1,000
42
43 ---------------------------------------------------------------
44 Answer Section:
45                            Sales Budget
46                            ------------
47                                   June      July     August
48                                   ------    ------   ------
49          Units                    FORMULA1       0          0
50          Dollars                  FORMULA2       0          0
51
52                     Unit Purchases Budget
53                     ---------------------
54                                   June      July     August
55                                   ------    ------   ------
56 Desired ending inventory          FORMULA3       0          0
57 Current month's unit sales        FORMULA4       0          0
58                                   --------  -------- --------
59 Total units needed                FORMULA5       0          0
60 Beginning inventory               FORMULA6       0          0
61                                   --------  -------- --------
62 Purchases (units)                 FORMULA7       0          0
63                                   ======== ======== ========
64 Purchases (dollars)               FORMULA8      $0         $0
65                                   ======== ======== ========
66
```

```
 67                           Cash Budget
 68                           -----------
 69                                      June      July    August
 70                                     ------    ------    ------
 71 Cash balance, beginning             $8,000       $0        $0
 72 Cash receipts:
 73   Collections from customers:
 74     From April sales               FORMULA9
 75     From May sales                 FORMULA10FORMULA11
 76     From June sales                FORMULA12        0         0
 77     From July sales                                 0         0
 78     From August sales                                        0
 79                                    -------- -------- --------
 80   Total cash available                 $0       $0        $0
 81 Cash disbursements:
 82   Merchandise                    FORMULA13       $0        $0
 83   Variable expenses              FORMULA14        0         0
 84   Fixed expenses                 FORMULA15        0         0
 85   Interest paid                         0        0         0
 86                                    -------- -------- --------
 87   Total disbursements                  $0       $0        $0
 88                                    -------- -------- --------
 89 Cash balance before financing          $0       $0        $0
 90 Less:  Desired ending balance           0        0         0
 91                                    -------- -------- --------
 92 Excess (deficit) of cash over needs    $0       $0        $0
 93                                    -------- -------- --------
 94 Financing
 95   Borrowing                            $0       $0        $0
 96   Repayment                             0        0         0
 97                                    -------- -------- --------
 98 Total effects of financing             $0       $0        $0
 99                                    -------- -------- --------
100 Cash balance, ending                   $0       $0        $0
101                                    ======== ======== ========
102
```

```
103                Forecasted Income Statement
104              For Quarter Ended August 31, 19X5
105              ------------------------------------
106 Sales                                              FORMULA16
107 Cost of goods sold                                 FORMULA17
108                                                    --------
109 Gross profit                                       FORMULA18
110                                                    --------
111 Expenses:
112    Variable expenses                               FORMULA19
113    Fixed expenses                                  FORMULA20
114    Depreciation expense                            FORMULA21
115    Interest expense                                FORMULA22
116                                                    --------
117    Total expenses                                       $0
118                                                    --------
119 Net income                                              $0
120                                                    ========
121
122                Forecasted Balance Sheet
123                   August 31, 19X5
124              ------------------------
125 Assets:
126    Cash                                            FORMULA23
127    Accounts receivable                             FORMULA24
128    Merchandise inventory                           FORMULA25
129    Fixed assets (net)                              FORMULA26
130                                                    --------
131 Total assets                                            $0
132                                                    ========
133 Liabilities & equity:
134    Accounts payable                                FORMULA27
135    Loans payable                                           0
136    Owner's equity                                  FORMULA28
137                                                    --------
138 Total liabilities & equity                              $0
139                                                    ========
140 ------------------------------------------------------------
```

162

P22 FLEXIBLE BUDGETING (FLEXBUD)

STUDENT NAME _____

SECTION NUMBER _____

Coleman Brass Works has just completed an in-depth study of overhead costs. The firm normally operates between 2,600 and 3,600 labor hours each month. Budgeted costs for this range of activity are presented below:

Depreciation	$3,000
Maintenance	$1,300 plus $0.60 per direct labor hour
Indirect labor	$2,300 plus $0.20 per direct labor hour
Utilities	$3,000 plus $0.15 per direct labor hour
Indirect material	$0.20 per direct labor hour
Overtime	$2.50 for each direct labor hour in excess of 3,000 direct labor hours per month

During March, Coleman had planned to operate at 3,400 direct labor hours. Actual activity amounted to only 3,000 hours with the following costs:

Depreciation	$3,000
Maintenance	3,200
Indirect labor	3,240
Utilities	3,500
Indirect material	650
Overtime	210

All fixed cost elements remained as budgeted.

Required

1) The president of the company has asked you to analyze the overhead costs in March by preparing a report making comparisons of actual costs to the original (static) budget which was prepared using the budget data presented above. The vice president of operations is interested in a similar report, but one that utilizes flexible budgeting concepts. The template called FLEXBUD that follows these requirements has been provided for your assistance. Note that the initial problem data is already entered in the Data Section of the template.

2) Using the spaces provided below, enter the 12 formulas required to complete the template. FORMULA6 and FORMULA12 will utilize the @IF special function command discussed in Appendix C.

FORMULA1 _____	FORMULA7 _____
FORMULA2 _____	FORMULA8 _____
FORMULA3 _____	FORMULA9 _____
FORMULA4 _____	FORMULA10 _____
FORMULA5 _____	FORMULA11 _____
FORMULA6 _____	FORMULA12 _____

3) Load the spreadsheet program and then load the template FLEXBUD. Enter the 12 formulas in the appropriate cells. Save your results as FLEXBUD3 and use ALT P to print the template when done. *Check figure: Total flexible budget difference (cell H50), $750 unfavorable*

4) Comment on the differences between the static and flexible budget performance reports. Which budget is more useful in appraising the performance of the various persons charged with the responsibility for cost control? Why?

_____

_____

_____

_____

What-If Analysis

5) The following actual overhead costs were incurred in April:

Depreciation	$3,000
Maintenance	3,400
Indirect labor	3,330
Utilities	3,700
Indirect material	700
Overtime	1,250

Planned direct labor hours were 3,000. Actual direct labor hours were 3,500. Other budget data for April were identical to March except that fixed indirect labor costs have increased to $2,700 and variable utilities costs have increased to $0.20 per direct labor hour.

Prepare and print new budget reports for April. Remember to change the month in cell C8. Save your completed template as FLEXBUD5. Compare the two budget reports and comment on the differences disclosed between the static budget and flexible budget performance reports. Also, if you were to suggest a revision to the budget for May, which cost category seems most in need of revision? Assuming that the fixed cost component of this budgeted cost is already correct, what should the variable cost component be so that the budget equals actual? Try different values in the appropriate cell in the Data Section and write your answers below.

_____

_____

_____

_____

_____

Graphics

6) Retrieve FLEXBUD3 and press the F10 key. On the graph, lines are plotting the cost behavior patterns of four of the overhead costs from this problem. Examine the patterns, review the Data Section, and identify below which of the four costs each represents.

A _____

B _____

C _____

D _____

TEMPLATE TICKLER

Retrieve the FLEXBUD3 template. The controller of Coleman Brass Works has discovered that insurance costs were mistakenly omitted from the original template. Insert new lines for insurance costs (right under maintenance costs) and redo the March performance reports to include the following information about insurance costs:

Budget: $1,100 per month plus $0.40 per direct labor hour
Actual: $2,200

Save the completed file as FLEXBUDT. Print the results when done.

GRAPHICS TICKLER

Retrieve the FLEXBUD3 template. Type /Graph, Name, Create, ORIG, and press ENTER. Then press Reset and Graph. Prepare a bar graph which graphically represents the budget variances shown on both budgets. No graphics data table is needed. Use B31.B36 as the X-axis (shorten titles to fit), H31.H36 as the A-range, and H43.H48 as the B-range. Use all appropriate titles, legends, formats, etc. Save the graph as a PIC file called FLEXBUDG. Save the template again as FLEXBUD3. Print the graph.

MACRO TICKLER

Design a print macro named \R on the FLEXBUD3 template to print only the Answer Section of the template with a heading that includes the company name and title of the report.

```
FLEXBUD                 Student Name  =
                        Section Number =
------------------------------------------------------------------
A       B       C       D       E       F       G       H
------------------------------------------------------------------
 6 Data Section:
 7
 8    For Month of: March
 9
10                           Budget Data
11                      Fixed        Variable            Actual
12                      Portion   +  Portion*            Data
13                      -------      --------            --------
14    Depreciation      $3,000        --                $3,000
15    Maintenance        1,300       $.60                3,200
16    Indirect labor     2,300        .20                3,240
17    Utilities          3,000        .15                3,500
18    Indirect material               .20                  650
19    Overtime                       2.50 **               210
20
21       *per direct labor hour
22      **per monthly direct labor hours in excess of    3,000
23
24    Planned direct labor hours for the month           3,400
25    Actual direct labor hours for the month            3,000
26 ---------------------------------------------------------------
27 Answer Section:
28
29    Static Budget                  Budget   Actual  Difference
30    -------------                  --------  -------- ----------
31    Depreciation                   FORMULA1    $0        $0
32    Maintenance                    FORMULA2     0         0
33    Indirect labor                 FORMULA3     0         0
34    Utilities                      FORMULA4     0         0
35    Indirect material              FORMULA5     0         0
36    Overtime                       FORMULA6     0         0
37                                   -------   -------   -------
38                                      $0       $0        $0
39                                   =======   =======   =======
40
41    Flexible Budget                Budget   Actual  Difference
42    ---------------                --------  -------- ----------
43    Depreciation                   FORMULA7    $0        $0
44    Maintenance                    FORMULA8     0         0
45    Indirect labor                 FORMULA9     0         0
46    Utilities                      FORMULA10    0         0
47    Indirect material              FORMULA11    0         0
48    Overtime                       FORMULA12    0         0
49                                   -------   -------   -------
50                                      $0       $0        $0
51                                   =======   =======   =======
52 ---------------------------------------------------------------
```

166

Frey Industries manufactures a product whose standard direct materials and direct labor unit costs are as follows:

Direct materials: 4 pounds at $21 per pound	$84
Direct labor 8 hours at $7 per hour	56

Actual data for November:
    Actual production: 6,400 units
    Direct materials used in production: 26,200 pounds costing $546,270
    Direct labor: 50,000 hours costing $352,500

Required

1) What is the total actual cost of November's production? Based on the standards, what should it have cost? Compute the total difference (variance) between these two amounts.

_____

_____

_____

_____

_____

2) The president of Frey wants an analysis prepared to help explain why the variance computed in Requirement 1 above occurred. Using the template called DIRVAR that follows these requirements, calculate the material and labor variances for Frey. The problem requires you to enter the input in the Data Section, as well as formulas in the Answer Section.

3) Use the problem data above to determine the values to be entered as INPUT A, INPUT B, etc. in the Data Section of the template. For now, pencil them in on the printout of DIRVAR.

4) In the spaces provided below, write the formulas requested in the template. FORMULA1 has been done for you as an example.

FORMULA1 ___(H9-H10)*H13___   FORMULA5 _____

FORMULA2 _____   FORMULA6 _____

FORMULA3 _____   FORMULA7 _____

FORMULA4 _____

5) Load the spreadsheet program and then load the template DIRVAR. Enter the input values you have computed. Then enter the formulas where indicated on the template. For each variance, enter either U for unfavorable or F for favorable in column H. Save the completed template as DIRVAR5. Use ALT P to print the template when done. *Check figure: Material quantity variance (cell F29), $12,600 U*

What-If Analysis

6) The template you have developed will handle most simple variance analysis problems. Try the problem below for NGP, Inc.:

	Cost Per Unit	
	Standard	Actual
Direct materials:		
Standard: 1.25 pounds $8 per pound	$10.00	
Actual: 1.20 pounds $8.50 per pound		$10.20
Direct labor:		
Standard: 2.5 hours at $5.50 per hour	13.75	
Actual: 3 hours at $5.30 per hour		15.90

Actual production for November was 10,500 units. Compute the direct materials and direct labor variances for NGP, Inc. **Indicate whether each variance is favorable or unfavorable.** Be careful when entering your input because this problem presents the information in a different format from the Frey Industry's data. Use ALT P to print the template when done.

Graphics

7) Retrieve DIRVAR5 and press the F10 key. On the screen is a graphical representation of the variances computed in Requirement 5. Review the graph and answer the following questions:

a. Which variances does each bar represent?

A _____

B _____

C _____

D _____

b. Which of the variances shown would be of most concern to management for immediate attention? (Consider groups of variances and materiality, also.) Explain:

_____

_____

_____

_____

_____

_____

_____

_____

_____

_____

TEMPLATE TICKLER

Retrieve DIRVAR5. Frey Industries also has the following information regarding overhead for November: actual overhead $315,000, standard variable overhead of $2 per direct labor hour, and standard fixed overhead of $4 per direct labor hour (based on 52,000 budgeted). Modify the template to compute all appropriate overhead variances. Save the completed template as DIRVART. Print the results when done.

Hint: Insert several new rows in the Data Section and in the Answer Section. Be sure to format cells in the appropriate manner.

GRAPHICS TICKLER

Retrieve the DIRVAR5 template. Type /Graph, Name, Create, **ORIG**, and press ENTER. Then press **Reset** and **Graph**. Prepare a stacked-bar graph to compare total standard cost per unit with actual cost per unit. Complete the graphics data table in rows 48 through 51 and use it as a basis for preparing the graph. The A-range should be material cost per unit, and the B-range should be labor cost. You do not need to use cell references when completing the graphics data table. Enter all appropriate titles, legends, and formats. Save the graph as a PIC file called DIRVARG. Save the template again as DIRVAR5. Print the graph.

MACRO TICKLER

Design a macro named **\R** on the DIRVAR5 template to automatically erase the input items in the Data Section and column H in the Answer Section. This macro could be used at the beginning of each month to erase last month's data and leave a "clean" template for the current month.

```
DIRVAR                 Student Name   =
                       Section Number =
------------------------------------------------------------------
 A      B       C       D       E       F       G       H
------------------------------------------------------------------
 6 Data Section:

 7

 8 Materials price variance input
 9   Actual cost of material per pound (ounce, etc.)    INPUT A
10   Standard cost of mat. per pound (ounce, etc.)      INPUT B
11

12 Materials quantity variance input
13   Actual quantity of materials used                  INPUT C
14   Standard quantity of mat. used for actual output   INPUT D
15

16 Labor rate variance input
17   Actual cost of labor per hour                      INPUT E
18   Standard cost of labor per hour                    INPUT F
19

20 Labor efficiency variance input
21   Actual quantity of hours incurred                  INPUT G
22   Standard quantity of hours for actual output       INPUT H
23

24 -------------------------------------------------------------
25 Answer Section:

26                                                      Indicate
27                                                      F or U
28 Material price variance        FORMULA1
29 Material quantity variance     FORMULA2
30                                   -------
31 Total materials variance                 FORMULA3
32

33 Labor rate variance           FORMULA4
34 Labor efficiency variance     FORMULA5
35                                   -------
36 Total labor variance                     FORMULA6
37                                            -------
38 Total materials and labor variances      FORMULA7
39                                          =======
40 -------------------------------------------------------------
```

Bridget's Bridal and Formal Store has divided its operations into two departments: Bridal, devoted to selling wedding apparel, and Formal, devoted to selling formal wear. Departmental expense accounts are kept for direct expenses, but indirect expenses are not allocated until the end of the accounting period. Selected data at March 31, 19X5, the end of the current fiscal year, are as follows:

	Formal	Bridal	Indirect Expenses
Departmental operating expenses:			
Sales salaries	$15,000	$25,000	
Rent			$ 12,000
Administrative salaries			20,000
Advertising	3,000	2,500	500
Supplies used	1,123	1,575	
Payroll taxes (5% of salaries)			3,000
Insurance expense			1,200
Depreciation expense	200	250	
Miscellaneous expense	225	180	100
	$19,548	$29,505	$ 36,800
	=====	=====	======

	Formal	Bridal	Totals
Other departmental data:			
Net sales	$55,000	$135,000	$190,000
Cost of goods sold	24,000	60,000	84,000
Average inventory	15,000	17,000	32,000
Floor space (square feet)	900	900	1,800
Equipment (original cost)	2,880	3,250	6,130

The bases for allocating indirect expenses are as follows:

Indirect Expense	Basis of Allocation
Rent	Floor space
Administrative salaries	Gross profit
Advertising	Net sales
Payroll taxes	Direct and indirect salaries
Insurance expense	Sum of equipment and average inventory
Miscellaneous expense	Supplies used

Required

1) As the accountant for Bridget's Bridal and Formal Store, you have been asked to prepare a departmental income statement. Review template DEPT that follows these requirements. All of the problem information relating to direct expenses has been entered into the Answer Section. You will be allocating the indirect expenses to the appropriate departments.

2) In the spaces provided below, write the formulas requested. FORMULA1 has been provided for you as an example.

FORMULA1   __(E25/G25)*F10__   FORMULA6 _____

FORMULA2 _____   FORMULA7 _____

FORMULA3 _____   FORMULA8 _____

FORMULA4 _____   FORMULA9 _____

FORMULA5 _____   FORMULA10 _____

3) Load the spreadsheet program and then load the template DEPT. Enter the formulas where indicated on the template. The cells that contain zeros now have been preprogrammed. They will change to non-zero values as the formulas are entered. Use ALT P to print the template when done. Save your template as DEPT3. *Check figure: Operating income, Bridal Department (cell G57), $22,336*

4) What conclusions can be drawn from this departmental income statement?

_____

_____

_____

_____

_____

_____

_____

_____

What-If Analysis

5) The sales manager for the Formal Department maintains that rent should be allocated on the basis of net sales rather than on floor space. The manager thinks this is fairer since the Bridal Department occupies more "prime location" floor space than does the Formal Department. Alter FORMULA1 and FORMULA2 (cells F48 and G48 respectively) on the template to see what effect this "fairer" allocation would have on each department's operating income. Use ALT P to print the template when done. Save the revision as DEPT5.

6) Comment on the results of this change and on the appropriateness of the new allocation scheme.

_____

_____

_____

_____

_____

_____

_____

_____

Graphics

7) The sales manager of the Formal Department, Barbara Severs, feels she has her direct expenses under control, but she is still concerned with the amount of indirect expenses allocated to her department. She has prepared a graph showing the percentage of sales made by her department and the percentage of expenses incurred. Retrieve DEPT3 and press the F10 key, then retrieve DEPT5 and press the F10 key. Is her concern warranted? Explain.

_____

_____

_____

_____

_____

TEMPLATE TICKLER

Retrieve the DEPT3 template. Bridget is considering whether the Formal Department should be eliminated. She wants to see departmental income statements which show each department's contribution toward indirect expenses. Modify the template so that it can help her with this decision. Save the revision as DEPTT and print the template when done. Should the Formal Department be eliminated? Explain.

_____

_____

_____

_____

_____

Hint: Insert rows and formulas to subtotal the direct expenses. Use these amounts to determine departmental contribution. Do not allocate the indirect expenses (i.e., erase all allocation formulas and redo the formulas in the total column).

GRAPHICS TICKLER

Retrieve the DEPT3 template. Type /Graph, Name, Create, ORIG, and press ENTER. Then press Reset and Graph. Prepare two pie graphs, one of which shows the composition of expenses for the Formal Department (cost of goods sold, total direct expenses, and total allocated indirect expenses), and the other for the Bridal Department. Complete the graphics data table in rows 65 to 69 and use it as a basis for preparing the graph. Use B67.B69 as the X-axis. Enter an appropriate title for each. Graph Name the graphs FORMAL and BRIDAL and Graph Save them under the same names. Save the template again as DEPT3. Print both graphs.

MACRO TICKLER

Design a macro named \R on the DEPT3 template to print your name and the Answer Section only.

```
------------------------------------------------------------
A      B       C       D       E       F       G       H
------------------------------------------------------------
```

 6 Data Section:
 7
 8   Indirect Expenses
 9   --
10   Rent $12,000
11   Administrative salaries   20,000
12   Advertising   500
13   Payroll taxes   3,000
14   Insurance expense   1,200
15   Miscellaneous expense   100
16   --
17
18   Other Departmental Data
19 --
20   Formal   Bridal   Totals
21   ------   ------   ------
22 Net sales $55,000 $135,000 $190,000
23 Cost of goods sold   24,000   60,000   84,000
24 Average inventory   15,000   17,000   32,000
25 Floor space (square feet) 900   900   1,800
26 Equipment (original cost) 2,880   3,250   6,130
27 --
28
29 --
30 Answer Section:
31   Bridget's Bridal & Formal Store
32   Departmental Income Statement
33   March 31, 19X5
34 --
35   Formal   Bridal   Totals
36   ------   ------   ------
37 Net sales $55,000 $135,000 $190,000
38 Cost of goods sold   24,000   60,000   84,000
39   -------- -------- --------
40 Gross profit $31,000 $75,000 $106,000
41   -------- -------- --------
42 Operating expenses:
43   Sales salaries $15,000 $25,000 $40,000
44   Advertising (direct) 3,000   2,500   5,500
45   Supplies used   1,123   1,575   2,698
46   Depreciation on equipment 200   250   450
47   Miscellaneous expense (direct) 225 180   405
48   Rent   FORMULA1 FORMULA2 FORMULA3
49   Administrative salaries FORMULA4 FORMULA5 FORMULA6
50   Advertising (indirect) FORMULA7   0   0
51   Payroll taxes   FORMULA8   0   0
52   Insurance expense   0 FORMULA9   0
53   Miscellaneous expenses (indirect) 0 FORMULA10 0
54   -------- -------- --------
55   Total operating expenses $0 $0 $0
56   -------- -------- --------
57 Operating income $0 $0 $0
58   ======== ======== ========
59 --
```

174
```

P25 CAPITAL BUDGETING
(CAPBUD)

STUDENT NAME _____

SECTION NUMBER _____

The owner of a tanning salon is considering renting space in a shopping mall for a new salon called Tanya's Tone-N-Tan. It is anticipated that this rental will require an investment in furniture, fixtures, and equipment costing $120,000 which has an estimated salvage value of $8,000 at the end of its useful life in 10 years. The new store is expected to generate annual cash flow of $25,000. The owner desires a 20% annual return on investment and wants a payback period of less than four years. Ignore the impact of taxes.

Required

1) Use the template called CAPBUD that follows these requirements to evaluate this investment for the owner. Note that the investment information is already entered in the Data Section of the template. Note also that there is a Scratch Pad at the bottom of the worksheet. The numbers are not a part of the Answer Section. They are needed as input to the net present value and internal rate of return calculations.

2) In the spaces provided below, enter the four formulas requested. Carefully review Appendix C for instructions on using the @NPV and @IRR special function commands.

FORMULA1 _____   FORMULA3 _____

FORMULA2 _____   FORMULA4 _____

3) Load Lotus 1-2-3 and then load the template CAPBUD. Enter the above formulas. Save the results as CAPBUD3 and use ALT P to print the results. *Check figure: Internal rate of return (cell G19), 16.58%*

4) Should the owner make the investment in the new shop? Explain.

_____

_____

_____

_____

_____

_____

What-If Analysis

5) The owner would like to test the sensitivity of the estimates used for the input data to compute the net present value and internal rate of return on this investment. Ignore the payback period and the accounting rate of return. Consider *a*, *b*, and *c* below independently by holding everything else constant:

a. What is the minimum cost of the investment (to the nearest $100) needed for the owner to accept it?

_____

b. Reset cost to $120,000. What is the minimum salvage value (to the nearest $100) needed for the owner to accept it?

_____

c. Reset salvage value to $8,000. What is the minimum annual cash flow (to the nearest $100) needed for the owner to accept it?

_____

Comment on the results of these analyses. How sensitive is the decision to accept or reject this investment to the estimates used for input data?

_____

_____

_____

_____

_____

_____

_____

6) Tanya's Tone-N-Tan's owner is also considering introducing a biofeedback service. The company will have to spend $35,000 for equipment, $2,000 for installation, and $7,000 for testing. The equipment will have no salvage value at the end of four years. Estimated annual results for the project are

Service fees		$52,000
Expenses other than depreciation	$33,000	
Depreciation (straight line)	_11,000_	_44,000_
Net income		$ 8,000
		=====

Enter the new information in the Data Section. Assuming the owner's criteria for accepting a project have not changed, should Tanya's Tone-N-Tan invest in this service? Explain. Use ALT P to print the template.

_____

_____

_____

_____

_____

_____

Graphics

7) Retrieve the CAPBUD3 template. In Requirement 5, you assessed the sensitivity of the investment's internal rate of return to changes in some of the input data. This was done in a trial-and-error fashion. Press the F10 key. Presented on the screen is a graphical analysis of the sensitivity of the internal rate of return to changes in annual cash flows. To demonstrate the usefulness of such a graph, note the ease with which you are able to answer the following questions which might be of interest to the owner:

a. What annual cash flow (approximately) is required to

   1) earn 0% rate of return? _____

2) earn 20% rate of return? _____

3) earn over 30% rate of return? _____

4) earn between 10% and 20% rate of return? _____

b. Approximately, how much is the rate of return reduced for each drop of $10,000 annual cash flow?

_____

TEMPLATE TICKLER

The template handles only cash inflows that are even in amount each year. Many capital projects generate uneven cash inflows. Retrieve CAPBUD3. Suppose that the project had cash earnings of $20,000 per year for the first two years, $30,000 for the next five years, and $60,000 for the last three years. Alter the template so that the NPV and IRR calculations can be made whether there are even or uneven cash flows. Save the completed template as CAPBUDT. Print the results.

Hint: One suggestion is to label column F in the Scratch Pad as UNEVEN CASH FLOW. Enter the uneven cash flows for each year. Modify FORMULA3 to include these cash flows. Modify the formulas in the range G33.G42 to include the new data. Now set cell G11 (estimated Annual Cash Inflow) to zero. When you have even cash flows, use cell G11 and set column F in the Scratch Pad to zeros. If you have uneven cash flows, set cell G11 to zero and fill in column F in the Scratch Pad.

Note that this solution causes garbage to come out in cells G16 and G17 because those formulas were not altered. There are other ways this problem can be solved.

GRAPHICS TICKLER

Retrieve the CAPBUD3 template. Type /Graph, Name, Create, ORIG, and press ENTER. Then press Reset and Graph. Develop a line graph just like the one used in Requirement 7 to show the sensitivity of net present value to changes in cost of the investment amount from $90,000 to $120,000 (use $5,000 increments). Complete the graphics table in cells E49 to F59 as a basis for preparing the graph. Save the graph as a PIC file called CAPBUDG. Save the template again as CAPBUD3. Print the graph.

MACRO TICKLER

The owner of Tanya's Tone-N-Tan wants this template to print out with the Answer Section first followed by the Data Section. Design a print macro named \R on template CAPBUD3 to accomplish this.

CAPBUD

```
------------------------------------------------------------------------
A       B       C       D       E       F       G       H
------------------------------------------------------------------------
```

 6 Data Section:
 7
 8 Cost of investment (initial outlay) $120,000
 9 Estimated life of investment   10   years
10 Estimated salvage value $8,000
11 Estimated annual cash inflow $25,000
12 Required rate of return   20.00%
13 --
14 Answer Section:
15
16   Payback period   FORMULA1   years
17   Accounting (average) rate of return   FORMULA2
18   Net present value   FORMULA3
19   Internal rate of return   FORMULA4
20 --
21
22
23
24
25 XXXXXXXXXXXXXXXXXXXXXXXXXXXXXXXXXXXXXXXXXXXXXXXXXXXXXXXXXXXXXXXXXX
26 Scratch Pad--Cash flow table needed for NPV & IRR calculations
27

28			NPV			IRR
29			-----------------			-----------
30			Annual	Salvage		Combined
31	Year		Cash Flow	Value		Flows
32	0					-120000
33	1		25000	0		25000
34	2		25000	0		25000
35	3		25000	0		25000
36	4		25000	0		25000
37	5		25000	0		25000
38	6		25000	0		25000
39	7		25000	0		25000
40	8		25000	0		25000
41	9		25000	0		25000
42	10		25000	8000		33000
```
```

MODEL-BUILDING PROBLEMS

MODEL-BUILDING CHECKLIST

Before submitting any model-building solution to your instructor, review the following list to assure that your template is presented in a clear, concise manner.

1. Enter your name in cell A1 and the name of the template file in cell A2. (Use the file name given in the problem.)

2. Include the name of the company, the name of the statement or schedule presented, and the date (i.e., 19X3, 4th Quarter, June). The date should be in an unprotected cell.

3. Use cell references in your formulas wherever possible.

4. Format all cells properly. Use the currency format at the top of all amount columns and below all subtotal rules.

5. Use 0 decimal places whenever decimal accuracy is not required. Generally, if the problem statement does not include cents, your answer will not require cents.

6. Vary column widths to fit the data presented.

7. Place titles at the top of all data columns (one exception is on financial statements where the statement heading is sufficient). Titles should be centered or right justified in the columns.

8. Use Data Sections wherever appropriate. If a Data Section is used, it must be labeled as such.

9. Use global worksheet protection on the worksheet. Unprotect the cells where changeable data or labels are to be entered.

10. Make underlines and double underlines the same width as the data.

11. Do not number the rows in column A or enter letters in row 5 as was done with the preprogrammed problems, unless your instructor directs you to do so.

12. Use upper and lowercase letters as appropriate. Generally uppercase letters are needed as the first letter in all headings and titles.

13. Use the @ROUND function to eliminate rounding discrepancies.

14. Print templates with no unusual spacing or gaps. Wide templates should be printed using compressed mode, if possible. Long templates should be printed with appropriate page breaks (1 page = 66 rows).

15. **(Optional)** Write a print macro named \P for each template that will print the template, and if required, print the formulas (/PPOOC).

The general ledger of Watson's Clothing Store shows the following account balances at June 30:

Cash	$ 2,005
Accounts receivable	5,850
Prepaid insurance	1,200
Accounts payable	1,900
Mark Watson, capital	10,000
Mark Watson, drawing	8,000
Revenue	17,080
Rent expense	8,000
Salary expense	2,950
Supplies expense	504
Utilities expense	366
Miscellaneous expense	105

Mr. Watson has asked you to develop a template that will serve as a trial balance (file name TB). Use the data above as input for your model. *Check figure: $28,980*

To test your model, use the following balances at July 31:

Cash	$ 1,202
Accounts receivable	7,871
Prepaid insurance	1,100
Accounts payable	995
Mark Watson, capital	10,000
Mark Watson, drawing	9,000
Revenue	21,450
Rent expense	9,200
Salary expense	2,890
Supplies expense	672
Utilities expense	402
Miscellaneous expense	108

Check figure: $32,445

Graphics (optional)

Using the test data template, prepare a pie graph showing the percentage of each asset to total assets. Print the graph when done.

The ledger of Brady Technologies showed the following balances after adjustment on July 31, 19X8, the end of the current fiscal year:

Accounts payable	$ 50,400	General expenses	$ 74,900
Accounts receivable	69,260	Interest expense	4,500
Accumulated depreciation--		Merchandise inventory	105,000
equipment	17,500	Prepaid insurance	6,750
E. Brady, Capital	221,090	Salaries payable	9,800
Cash	53,580	Sales	629,000
Cost of merchandise sold	414,300	Selling expenses	92,500
Equipment	95,000	Withdrawals	12,000

The president of Brady has asked you to develop a financial statement template (file name FS) that includes an income statement, a statement of owner's equity, and a balance sheet. This template will allow the financial statements to be prepared quickly by entering account balances in the appropriate cells on the template. Use the information above as input for your template. *Check figure: Total assets, $312,090*

To test your model, use the following data for the year ended July 31, 19X9:

Accounts payable	$ 44,700	General expenses	$ 72,100
Accounts receivable	61,800	Interest expense	6,000
Accumulated depreciation--		Merchandise inventory	80,500
equipment	19,600	Prepaid insurance	7,200
E. Brady, Capital	251,890	Salaries payable	8,300
Cash	49,700	Sales	595,000
Cost of merchandise sold	439,890	Selling expenses	86,300
Equipment	98,000	Withdrawals	18,000

Check figure: Total assets, $277,600

Graphics (optional)

Utilizing the test data template, prepare a pie graph depicting the various expenses incurred by Brady Technologies. Print the graph when done.

The terms of sales on account offered by Happy's Hardware Store are 2/10, n/30. During the first week of May, the following transactions involved receiving cash:

May 1   Received $529.20 from Burns Inc. in payment of an April 22 invoice of $540, less discount.

    3   Received a loan of $3,000 from First National Bank.

    4   Received $372.15 from Screw World in payment of an April 23 invoice.

    5   Received $481.18 from King Corp. in payment of an April 28 invoice of $491, less discount.

    7   Cash sales for the week totaled $8,000.

Happy's Hardware Store has asked you to create a computerized cash receipts journal (file name CRJ). The journal should include one column each for the date, account name, Sundry Accounts Cr., Sales Cr., Accounts Receivable Cr., Sales Discount Dr., and Cash Dr. The appropriate columns should be totaled. Use the data for the first week in May as input for the template. *Check figure: Total cash debits, $12,382.53*

To test your model, use the following information for the second week of May:

May 8   Received $284.20 from ABC Inc. in payment of a May 1 invoice of $290, less discount.

    9   Received $597.80 from Screw World in payment of an April 28 invoice of $610, less discount.

    12   Received $475.15 from Byn Stores in payment of a May 1 invoice.

    13   Received $100 for old store equipment that had no book value.

    14   Cash sales for the week totaled $6,000.

Check figure: Total cash debits, $7,457.15

Graphics (optional)

Using your test model, create a bar graph showing the amount of cash Happy collected from each customer the second week of May. Print the graph when done.

Selected data on merchandise inventory, purchases, and sales for Wheeler Enterprises for the month of December are as follows:

	Cost	Retail
Merchandise inventory, December 1	$105,900	$199,400
Purchases	63,200	120,600
Purchases returns and allowances	1,100	---
Sales		126,600
Sales returns and allowances		3,500

Develop a template that uses the retail method to automatically compute an estimate of ending inventory (file name RETAIL). The flexibility of your template could be greatly enhanced by using a Data Section. Use the December data above as input for your template. *Check figure: Ending inventory at approximate cost, $103,373*

To test your model, use the following data for January:

	Cost	Retail
Merchandise inventory, January 1	$101,588	$193,500
Purchases	60,500	138,800
Purchases returns and allowances	1,700	---
Sales		200,000
Sales returns and allowances		4,000

Check figure: Ending inventory at approximate cost, $65,787

Graphics (optional)

Design a bar graph that depicts merchandise available for sale at cost and at retail for both December and January. Print the graph when done.

Information about Cedar Company's inventory at April 30, is as follows:

Commodity	Inventory Quantity	Unit Cost	Unit Market
A	50	$160	$155
B	110	205	220
C	29	100	103
D	80	70	60

You have been asked to develop a template that will determine the value of the inventory on an item-by-item basis at the lower of cost or market value (file name LCOM). You should find it helpful to use the @MIN function discussed in Appendix C. Use the data above as input for your template. *Check figure: Lower of cost or market inventory value, $38,000*

———————————————————————————————

To test your model, use the following information about Cedar's inventory at July 31:

Commodity	Inventory Quantity	Unit Cost	Unit Market
A	60	$160	$162
B	95	205	210
C	30	100	98
D	107	70	65

Check figure: Lower of cost or market inventory value, $38,970

Graphics (optional)

From the test data template, design a bar graph demonstrating the relationship between "total cost" and "total market value" for each commodity. Print the graph when done.

———————————————————————————————

Information about one of Corky Manufacturing's plant assets, a snowplow, is as follows:

Cost	$5,000
Estimated residual value	400
Depreciation method	Straight-line
Date purchased	10/01/X1
Estimated life	10 years

The company has hired you to develop a computerized subsidiary ledger form for plant assets (file name PAR). A separate ledger account is to be maintained for each asset. Your form should contain basic facts about the asset (such as date purchased, etc.), depreciation charged each period, accumulated depreciation-to-date, and book value. The model you develop should automatically update the book value of the asset after each entry. Record the acquisition of the machine and depreciation through 19X3. Assume that the firm's annual accounting cycle ends on December 31. *Check figure: Book value of snowplow, $3,965*

To test your model, use the following information for a door processor:

Cost	$8,000
Estimated residual value	200
Depreciation method	Sum-of-the-years-digits
Date purchased	01/01/X1
Estimated life	12 years

Check figure: Book value of door processor, $4,700

Graphics (optional)

Using the test data, prepare a line graph showing the book value of the door processor from date of purchase to 12/31/X3. Print the graph when done.

In 19X2, Newsome Contracting was working on several contracts. Relevant information about one of the projects is as follows:

Contract A:	Total contract price	$9,300,000
	Total anticipated costs	6,450,217
	Costs incurred during current year	550,821

Newsome Contracting realizes the revenue from destruction contracts by the percentage-of-contract-completion method. The company measures percentages-of-contract-completion by the ratio of current period construction costs to total anticipated construction costs. Newsome has hired you to develop a template (file name PERCOM) that will quickly and accurately compute current year profit on any of its contracts at any time. Your template should include a Data Section. Use the information for Contract A as input for your model. *Check figure: Current year profit from Contract A, $243,359*

To test your model, use the following information for Contract B:

Contract B:	Total contract price	$6,555,555
	Total anticipated costs	3,444,555
	Costs incurred during current year	2,343,231

Check figure: Current year profit from Contract B, $2,116,323

Graphics (optional)

Prepare a stacked-bar graph showing how total contract price is broken down between total anticipated costs and total anticipated profits for contracts A and B. Print the graph when done.

M8 • PARTNERSHIP: DIVISION OF NET INCOME

H. Horto and P. Moss recently formed a partnership. Horto invested $20,000 cash, and Moss invested $20,000 of plant assets and $10,000 cash. The partners are trying to find an equitable way of splitting the income to take into account that Moss invested more capital, but Horto will spend twice as much time as Moss in running the business. They have asked you to develop a template (file name PSHIP) to allow them to see the effect of:

1) Various interest rates on invested capital
2) Various salary allowances for time spent
3) Various levels of partnership net income

The easiest way to achieve this flexibility is to use a Data Section. Use the following information as input for your model:

Net income	$75,000
Division of net income:	
Interest on original investments at 15%	
Salary allowances:	
Horto	35,000
Moss	20,000
Remainder shared equally	

Check figure: Horto net income, $44,250

To test your model, use the following profit-sharing scenario:

Net income	$125,000
Division of net income:	
Interest on original investments at 25%	
Salary allowances:	
Horto	35,000
Moss	17,000
Remainder shared equally	

Check figure: Horto net income, $70,250

Graphics (optional)

Using the test data provided, prepare a stacked-bar graph showing the division of net income (salary, interest, and remainder) to each partner. Print the graph when done.

The following data were selected from the records of Dandy's Candyland, Inc. for the month ended March 31:

Advertising expense	$ 20,200	Loss from disposal of a segment	
Depreciation expense--office equipment	1,000	of business	46,000
Depreciation expense--store equipment	5,000	Merchandise inventory, March 1	150,000
Extraordinary loss	20,000	Merchandise inventory, March 31	136,000
Income tax:		Office salaries expense	34,000
On continuing operations	30,000	Office supplies expense	2,050
Reduction applicable to loss from		Purchases	600,000
disposal of a segment of the business	9,000	Rent expense	1,000
Reduction applicable to		Sales	905,000
extraordinary loss	2,200	Sales salaries expense	30,000
Insurance expense	1,000	Store supplies expense	5,050
Interest expense	5,000		

This firm's accounting system generates these totals on a monthly basis. You have been asked to develop a template (file name IS) that will allow a monthly income statement to be prepared by entering monthly figures in the appropriate cells. The income statement should include a section for earnings per share. There were 20,000 shares of common stock (no preferred) outstanding throughout the month. Use the data above as input for your template. *Check figure: March net income, $101,900*

To test your model, use the following data for the month ended April 30:

Advertising expense	$ 23,000	Loss from disposal of a segment of business	
Depreciation expense--office equipment	1,620	(additional expenses from	
Depreciation expense--store equipment	6,470	March disposal)	2,000
Extraordinary loss		Merchandise inventory, April 1	136,000
(additional expenses from March loss)	15,000	Merchandise inventory, April 30	140,000
Income tax:		Office salaries expense	40,000
On continuing operations	20,000	Office supplies expense	1,870
Reduction applicable to loss from		Purchases	502,400
disposal of a segment of the business	800	Rent expense	2,000
Reduction applicable to		Sales	700,000
extraordinary loss	3,200	Sales salaries expense	52,500
Insurance expense	1,000	Store supplies expense	6,300
Interest expense	12,000		

There was no change in the number of shares of common stock outstanding. *Check figure: April net income, $21,840*

Graphics (optional)

From the test data template, develop a pie graph that presents the percentage distribution of selling expenses. Print the graph when done.

A prospective investor has hired you to develop a template that will compute the book value per share (file name BVALUE) on each class of stock of various companies. Your template should include a Data Section.

One of the companies the investor is currently interested in is Stevens Corporation which has the following capital structure:

Preferred 14% stock, $35 par	$1,050,000
Premium on preferred stock	64,000
Common stock, $30 par	1,350,000
Premium on common stock	82,000
Retained earnings	350,000

Preferred stock has a prior claim to assets on liquidation to the extent of 120% of par. *Check figure: Book value per share, Stevens Corporation: Common, $36.36*

To test your model, use the following data for Ramirez Restaurant, Inc.:

Preferred 12% stock, $45 par	$ 900,000
Premium on preferred stock	85,000
Common stock, $25 par	1,250,000
Premium on common stock	90,000
Retained earnings	325,000

Preferred stock has a prior claim to assets on liquidation to the extent of 110% of par. *Check figure: Book value per share, Ramirez Restaurant: Common, $33.20*

Graphics (optional)

Using the test template, prepare a pie graph that shows how much equity was allocated to preferred stock and how much was allocated to common stock. Print the graph when done.

M11 • CONSTANT DOLLAR INCOME STATEMENT

The following income statement was prepared from the records of Palmer Corporation at March 31, the end of the current fiscal year:

Palmer Corporation
Income Statement
For Year Ended March 31, 19X8

Revenue		$110,000
Expenses:		
Depreciation expense on equipment	$16,000	
Rent expense	10,000	
Supplies expense	3,000	
Wages expense	56,000	
Miscellaneous expense	900	85,900
Net income		$ 24,100

Revenue, miscellaneous expense, rent expense, and wages expense occurred evenly throughout the year. Equipment was acquired when the price index was 140, and supplies were acquired when the price index was 163. The price index averaged 156 for the year and was 164 at the end of the year. Develop a template (file name CDOLLAR) to translate Palmer's historical cost income statement into a constant dollar income statement. Use the data above as input for your model. The purchasing power loss on monetary items was $5,500. *Check figure: Constant dollar net income, $17,251*

To test your model, use the information below for the following year:

Palmer Corporation
Income Statement
For Year Ended March 31, 19X9

Revenue		$120,000
Expenses:		
Depreciation expense on equipment	$16,000	
Rent expense	13,000	
Supplies expense	2,000	
Wages expense	62,500	
Miscellaneous expense	800	94,300
Net income		$ 25,700

Revenue, miscellaneous expense, rent expense, and wages expense occurred evenly throughout the year. Equipment was acquired when the price index was 140, and supplies were acquired when the price index was 165. The price index averaged 160 for the year and was 168 at year end. The purchasing power loss on monetary items was $5,000. *Check figure: Constant dollar net income, $19,649*

Graphics (optional)

Utilizing the test data, create a pie graph showing the proportionate breakdown of total restated expenses for the year. Print the graph when done.

Differences in accounting methods between those applied to its accounts and those used in determining taxable income yielded the following amounts for the first three years of Marshall Steel Productions:

	First Year	Second Year	Third Year
Income before income tax	$375,000	$409,000	$431,000
Taxable income	359,000	415,000	420,000

The income tax rate for each of the three years was 40% of taxable income, and taxes were paid promptly each year. The president of Marshall has asked you to develop a template (file name DEFERTAX) that will show income tax deducted on income statement, income tax payments for the year, year's addition to (deduction from) deferred income tax payable, and the year-end balance of deferred income tax payable. Use the information above as input for the Data Section of your template. *Check figure: Marshall Steel Products, year-end balance of deferred tax payable, third year, $8,400*

The president of Central Products Company is impressed with your model and wishes to test it using the following data from Central Products (assume a 40% tax rate):

	First Year	Second Year	Third Year
Income before income tax	$438,000	$435,000	$475,000
Taxable income	418,000	440,000	450,000

Check figure: Central Products Company year-end balance of deferred tax payable, third year, $16,000

Graphics (optional)

Using the Central Products data, create a bar graph showing the annual addition to or reduction in deferred taxes for all three years. Print the graph when done.

Tammy and Tommy Turtlemeyer have one child and have contributed more than half of the cost of supporting Tammy's mother, who received gross income of $800 during the year. During the current year ended December 31, Tommy realized a net long-term capital gain of $3,600. Other details of receipts and disbursements during the year are as follows:

Tammy's gross salary	$52,000	Rental property:	
Tommy's gross salary	45,000	Real estate tax	$ 1,650
Dividends on corporation		Insurance	500
stock	400	Depreciation	1,210
Rent from property owned	8,000	Interest on mortgage	1,500
Interest on municipal bonds	550	Real estate tax on	
Safe deposit box rental	100	residence	5,500
State sales tax on items		Mortgage interest on	
purchased for personal use	550	residence	12,000
Automobile license fees	50	Charge account interest	400
Charitable contributions	1,700	City income taxes	900
Tax preparation fee	300	State income taxes	4,400
		Medical bills	1,000

You have been hired by a local CPA firm to design a template that will calculate taxable income for married couples filing joint returns (file name MFJ). Do not use a Data Section. Set up the template in a standard tax return format. Use the above data as input for your model. *No check figure because tax rules change each year*

To test your model, use the following information about Penelope and Patch Parker, who have three children and incurred a net long-term capital gain of $5,500:

Penelope's gross salary	$35,000	Rental property:	
Patch's gross salary	60,000	Real estate tax	$ 2,000
Dividends on corporation		Insurance	660
stock	500	Depreciation	1,400
Rent from property owned	9,200	Interest on mortgage	2,000
Interest on municipal bonds	400	Real estate tax on	
Safe deposit box rental	35	residence	4,500
State sales tax on items		Mortgage interest on	
purchased for personal use	500	residence	8,600
Automobile license fees	60	Charge account interest	450
Charitable contributions	1,000	City income taxes	760
Tax preparation fee	225	State income taxes	4,200
		Medical bills	2,750

No check figure because tax rules change each year

Graphics (optional)

Using the data from the test model, create a pie graph proportionately showing the various taxes claimed as itemized deductions by the Parkers. Print the graph when done.

M14 • BOND PREMIUM AND DISCOUNT AMORTIZATION SCHEDULE

On June 1, Richar Company issued $400,000 of 10-year, 14% bonds at an effective interest rate of 13%. This netted the company $421,705. Interest on the bonds is payable annually on June 1. The president of Richar has asked you to develop an amortization schedule template (file name AMORT) that will use the interest method to calculate annual interest expense, premium (or discount) amortization, unamortized premium (or discount), and bond carrying amount. Your template should include a Data Section. *Check figure: Amortization of $400,000 bonds premium in year 10, $3,540*

To test your model, calculate the annual interest expense, discount amortization, unamortized discount, and bond carrying amount of $300,000 of 10-year, 8% bonds at an effective interest rate of 9%. The issuance of these bonds netted the company $280,747. Interest on the bonds is payable annually. *Check figure: Amortization of $300,000 bonds discount in year 10, $2,752*

Graphics (optional)

With information from the test data, create a line graph that shows annual interest paid and interest expense over the 10-year life of the bond. Print the graph when done.

Bea Hamill manages several properties for real estate investors. Each month she reviews the cash flow statements from each property to look for trouble spots. Information for one of the properties, Severance Cross Apartments, is as follows:

Severance Cross
Statement of Cash Receipts and Expenses

Revenue:		
Rental revenue		$500,000
Vending machine revenue	5,000	
Total revenue	505,000	
Expenses:		
Advertising expense	$ 5,300	
Administrative expense	29,400	
Utilities expense		40,000
Maintenance and repairs expense	36,360	
Real estate tax expense	58,800	
Insurance expense	4,000	
Interest expense		206,000
Total expenses	379,860	
Net cash flow	$125,140	
	======	

Bea has asked you to develop a template that will automatically prepare a vertical analysis of the cash flow data (file name VERT). All percentages should be based on total revenue. Use the data above as input for your model. *Check figure: Severance Cross interest expense is 41% of total revenue.*

To test your model, use the following information for McCosh Manor. *Check figure: McCosh Manor interest expense is 21% of total revenue.*

McCosh Manor Bed and Breakfast
Statement of Cash Receipts and Expenses

Revenue:		
Rental revenue		$ 90,000
Vending machine revenue	6,620	
Total revenue	96,620	
Expenses:		
Advertising expense	$ 2,220	
Administrative expense	3,384	
Utilities expense		5,650
Maintenance and repairs expense	2,250	
Real estate tax expense	8,000	
Insurance expense	2,220	
Interest expense		20,000
	43,724	
Net cash flow	$ 52,896	
	======	

Graphics (optional)

Using the test data template, prepare a pie graph of the expenses. Use short titles for the X-axis. Print the graph when done.

At the present time, Appletree Technologies is preparing a bid for a contract to produce 2,000 doodlewickies. The deadline for bids is July 1. The predicted costs of production are as follows:

| | Direct Material | Direct Labor | |
Dept.	Amount	Hourly Rate	Hours
Assembly	$ 800	$15.00	100
Painting	5,000	16.00	300
Packaging	1,020	8.00	50

The president has asked you to develop a computerized job order cost sheet (file name JOB) that can be used to determine the company's bid on a particular contract. Factory overhead is applied at the rate of 60% of direct labor cost, and Appletree uses a 30% markup rate on total manufacturing cost in determining its bid prices. The cost sheet that you develop should include a heading with a description of the job and the deadline date for bidding. The template should be formatted to express all values except labor rates as integers. Use the data above as input for your template. *Check figure: Bid price on doodlewickies, $22,802*

To test your model, use the following data which pertains to a prospective contract to produce 10,000 mackelhorns (deadline for bids is December 15):

| | Direct Material | Direct Labor | |
Dept.	Amount	Hourly Rate	Hours
Assembly	$2,200	$15.50	300
Painting	900	17.00	100
Packaging	500	10.60	200

Check figure: Bid price on mackelhorns, $22,298

Graphics (optional)

Using your test model, design a pie graph that shows the proportionate amount of raw materials that each department uses. Print the graph when done.

An examination of monthly production and cost data over a period of several months for Emerald Industries reveals that the highest and lowest levels of production are as follows:

	Total Units Produced	Total Costs
Highest level	120,000	$275,000
Lowest level	50,000	170,000

It is estimated that 90,000 units will be produced next month. Develop a template (file name HL) that can be used to calculate variable cost per unit and total fixed cost using the high-low points method. Then use the estimate to calculate the estimated cost of producing next month's output. *Check figure: Estimated variable cost per unit for Emerald Industries, $1.50*

To test your model, use the following information from Donovan Company:

	Total Units Produced	Total Costs
Highest level	2,200	$29,400
Lowest level	1,200	22,300

Estimate the cost of producing 2,100 units. *Check figure: Estimated variable cost per unit for Donovan Company, $7.10*

Graphics (optional)

From the test data template, create an XY graph plotting the high and low points. Use units produced as the X-axis (X-axis range) and total costs as the Y-axis (A-range). Print the graph when done.

In 19X8, Nifty Company anticipates fixed costs of $200,000. Variable costs and expenses are expected to be 65% of sales. The president has asked you to develop a template to calculate sales needed to break-even and sales needed to achieve any desired net income (file name DESNI). Assume as initial input for your model that the company wishes to achieve a net income of $65,000. *Check figure: Sales needed for desired net income, $757,143*

To test your model, use the following projections for 19X9: Fixed costs of $250,000 and variable costs and expenses to equal 45% of sales. The company wishes to have a net income of $75,000. *Check figure: Sales needed for desired net income, $590,909*

Graphics (optional)

Using the test data template, develop a standard break-even chart (line graph) which plots total revenue and total costs from a sales level of $0 to $700,000. Use $100,000 increments on the X-axis.

Reinsch Corporation manufactures several products. In December of 19X8, the board of directors decided to raise the price of Product A from $40, which had prevailed throughout 19X8, to $44, effective January 1, 19X9. The comparative gross profits for Product A for 19X8 and 19X9 are as follows:

	19X9	19X8
Sales of Product A	$215,000	$217,500
Cost of goods sold	120,000	130,500
Gross profit	$ 95,000	$87,000
	======	======

The board is pleased with the increase in gross profit but would like to know what effect each of the following factors had on causing the increase:

1) Increase in selling price
2) Increase (if any) in unit sales volume
3) Decrease (if any) in unit costs

The president of Reinsch Corporation has asked you to develop a computerized gross profit analysis report (file name GPANAL). Your template should include a Data Section that contains sales, cost of goods sold, gross profit, and unit sales price for each year, as well as the change from one year to another for each. The template should also compute unit costs for each year and the number of units sold. *Check figure: Reduction of sales of product A attributed to decrease in quantity sold, $22,045*

To test your model, use the following information for Product B which sold for $27 in 19X8 and $28 in 19X9:

	19X9	19X8
Sales of Product B	$600,000	$500,000
Cost of goods sold	315,000	300,000
Gross profit	$285,000	$200,000
	======	======

Check figure: Increase in sales of product B attributed to increase in quantity sold, $78,571

Graphics (optional)

Using the test model template, design a bar graph showing how the dollar amount of each of the four variances contributed to the change in gross profit. Print the graph when done.

Hickory Products is concerned about its cash position at the end of November because of the anticipated inventory build up during that month to get ready for the holiday season. Selected information about expected November activity is presented below:

Cash balance, November	$ 9,000
Sales	140,000
Gross profit percent (based on sales)	40%
Decrease in accounts receivable during month	$ 8,000
Increase in accounts payable during month	34,000
Increase in inventory during month	60,000

Selling expenses total $31,000 per month plus 16% of sales. Variable selling expenses include estimated doubtful accounts equal to 1% of sales. Depreciation expense of $13,000 per month is included in fixed selling expenses.

Prepare a template (file name CASHBUD) which will allow Hickory to compute its projected cash balance at the end of November. Design the model so that it could be reused any month that Hickory wishes. *Check figure: Projected ending cash balance, $8,000*

To test your model, use the following estimates for December:

Cash balance, December 1	$ 8,000
Sales	180,000
Gross profit percent (based on sales)	35%
Increase in accounts receivable during month	$ 20,000
Increase in accounts payable during month	10,000
Decrease in inventory during month	24,000

Selling expenses total $37,000 per month plus 13% of sales. Variable selling expenses include estimated doubtful accounts equal to 1% of sales. Depreciation expense of $15,000 per month is included in fixed selling expenses. *Check figure: Projected ending cash balance, $41,400*

Graphics (optional)

Using the test template, prepare a bar graph showing the effects that sales, cost of goods sold, change in accounts receivable, change in accounts payable, and change in inventory have on the projected ending cash balance. Print the graph when done.

The Shoe Factory produces two kinds of shoes: soft and blue suede. Estimated production and sales data for December are as follows:

	Soft	Blue Suede
Beginning inventory (units), December 1	30,000	20,000
Desired inventory (units), December 31	20,000	40,000
Expected sales volume (units):		
East side store	14,000	25,000
West side store	10,000	20,000
Unit sales price	$ 1.50	$ 1.70

You have been asked to prepare a computerized sales budget (units and dollars) and a production budget (file name SPBUD). Use the data above as input for your model. *Check figure: Blue suede shoes required production, 65,000 units*

To test your model, use the following estimates for January:

	Soft	Blue Suede
Beginning inventory (units), January 1	12,000	30,000
Desired inventory (units), January 31	9,000	40,000
Expected sales volume (units):		
East side store	14,000	30,000
West side store	15,000	25,000
Unit sales price	$ 1.60	$ 2.00

Check figure: Blue suede shoes required production, 65,000 units

Graphics (optional)

Using the test model, prepare a pie graph depicting the percentage of dollar sales of soft shoes at the east side store as compared to the west side store. Print the graph when done.

Hamilton Factory Works makes bumpers for cars. During March, 8,000 bumpers were manufactured with standard costs and actual costs for direct materials, direct labor, and factory overhead as follows:

	Standard Costs	Actual Costs
Direct materials	5,000 pounds $8	5,300 pounds $ 9.25
Direct labor	10,000 hours $12	10,300 hours $11.75
Factory overhead	Rates per direct labor hour, based on normal capacity of 15,000 labor hours:	
	Variable cost $5.50	Variable cost $47,000
	Fixed cost $3.50	Fixed cost $45,000

You have been asked to develop a template that will calculate the quantity variance, price variance, total direct materials cost variance, time variance, rate variance, total direct labor cost variance, volume variance, controllable variance, and total factory overhead cost variance (file name VARIANCE). Use the information above as input for the Data Section of your template. *Check figure: Factory overhead volume variance, $17,500 U*

To test your model, use the following information for the manufacture of 12,000 bumpers during April:

	Standard Costs	Actual Costs
Direct materials	8,000 pounds $10	7,400 pounds $10.60
Direct labor	15,000 hours $14	14,200 hours $15.25
Factory overhead	Rates per direct labor hour, based on normal capacity of 15,000 labor hours:	
	Variable cost $5.50	Variable cost $83,000
	Fixed cost $3.50	Fixed cost $48,000

Check figure: Factory overhead volume variance, $0

Graphics (optional)

Using the test model template, create a bar graph that plots the four materials and labor variances (quantity, price, time, and rate). Print the graph when done.

Sandy's Soup 'n Serve is considering the replacement of a stove that the company has used for 4 years. Relevant data about the old and new machines are as follows:

Old Stove:

Cost (10-year life when purchased)	$3,500
Annual depreciation	350
Annual operating costs	5,000
Estimated current selling price	2,200

New stove:

Cost (6-year life)		$6,300
Annual depreciation	1,050	
Estimated annual operating costs	4,000	

Annual revenue is not expected to change if the new stove is purchased. You have been asked to develop a template that will calculate the net cost reduction or net cost increase associated with purchasing the new stove (file name REPLACE). Your analysis should include all six years. Assume no residual value at the end of six years for either machine. Some of the above data may be irrelevant to the replacement decision and need not be included in your model. Use the information above as input for the Data Section of your template. *Check figure: Net cost reduction for new stove, $1,900*

To test your model, use the following data. Sandy's Soup 'n Serve is considering replacing a dishwasher which it has been using for 2 years. Assume no residual value at the end of three years for either dishwasher.

Old Dishwasher:

Cost (5-year life when purchased)	$1,900
Annual depreciation	380
Annual operating costs	2,800
Estimated current selling price	1,050

New Dishwasher:

Cost (3-year life)		$2,100
Annual depreciation	700	
Estimated annual operating costs	2,600	

Check figure: Net cost increase for new dishwasher, $450

Graphics (optional)

Making use of the test data, prepare a bar graph that shows the annual operating costs of both dishwashers. Print the graph when done.

During the month of August, Nungen Furniture Store received the following amounts in payment of sales that took place in 19X7, 19X8, and 19X9:

Year of Sale	Amount Received this Month
19X7	$7,650
19X8	9,870
19X9	4,100

Nungen uses the installment method of accounting and recognizes gross profit based on the following historical rates:

32% for 19X7 sales
30% for 19X8 sales
27% for 19X9 sales

You are to develop a template (file name INSTALL) that will calculate the amount of net income recognized in August under the installment method described above. Assume that operating expenses for the month total $5,200. *Check figure: Net income realized, $1,316*

To test your model, use the following receipts for September, when operating expenses totaled $4,950:

Year of Sale	Amount Received this Month
19X7	$8,020
19X8	8,730
19X9	5,460

Check figure: Net income realized, $1,710

Graphics (optional)

Design a bar graph that shows amount received this month compared to gross profit recognized. Do this for all three years. Print the graph when done.

APPENDIX A
MICROCOMPUTER OPERATIONS

Operating a microcomputer is fairly easy. With a few simple instructions, you should have no problems at all.

IBM PC HARDWARE

An IBM PC system consists of a keyboard, a processing unit containing one or two floppy disk drives, and a monitor (TV screen). If there are two drives, the drive on the left (or on the top) is drive A, and the one on the right (or on the bottom) is drive B. If there is a hard disk, it is referred to as drive C. A printer may be attached to the system.

The IBM Personal System/2 consists of a keyboard, a processing unit containing a hard disk and a floppy disk drive, and a monitor. A second floppy disk drive may be included. The hard disk is referred to as drive C, and the floppy disk drive is referred to as drive A.

KEYBOARD

There are several keyboards available for use with microcomputers. The basic alphabet and number keys are located in standard positions. However, keys unique to microcomputer keyboards, such as Escape, Print Screen, Page Up and Page Down, may be located in different positions. The two most common keyboards that accompany IBM microcomputers are shown in Illustrations A-1 and A-2 on pages 211 and 212.

As you work through the tutorial, you may want to refer to these illustrations for the location of certain keys.

LOADING A PROGRAM

Computer programs like Lotus 1-2-3 are usually stored on disks. Loading a program means transferring the program from the disk to the processing unit. To load a program for a system with two floppy disk drives, use the following steps:

1. Before a program can be loaded, the disk operating system (DOS) must be loaded into the computer. This requires a separate DOS disk or a program disk which has had DOS placed on it. For example, DOS can be placed on the program (System) disk of Version 1A of Lotus 1-2-3, but not on Versions 2, 2.01, or 2.2.

    Insert the disk with DOS on it (either a separate DOS disk or a program disk with DOS) into drive A. If the latch over the slot in the drive is closed, open it. The disk should be inserted with the label upwards. With 5 1/4-inch disks, the edge of the disk with the oval cutout in the disk's square plastic cover should enter the drive first. With 3 1/2-inch disks, the edge of the disk with the metal plate should enter the drive first. The edge with the label should enter the drive last. A good rule to follow is to hold the disk with your thumb on the label.

    Push the disk gently until it is entirely in the drive. If you bend or force the disk, it can be permanently damaged. Close the disk drive latch. Never turn on the computer without a disk in the drive.

2. Turn on the computer. The switch is located on the right side of the processing unit toward the back. Also, make sure the monitor is on.

    The red light on the disk drive will come on, and the drive may make a lot of clacking and spinning noises. After a while, the red light will go out, and you may need to enter some information from the keyboard (for example, date and time). After each entry, the large key with the (⏎) symbol is pressed. This key is referred to as the ENTER key throughout this manual. The red light may go on and off several more times.

    If you used a program disk with DOS already on it, the program will now be loaded in the computer and will be ready to run. If you used a separate DOS disk, you will see the operating system prompt (A>) on the screen. This manual uses A> to represent the operating system prompt, but your prompt may look different. Remove the DOS disk and insert the program disk. Type the name of the program and press ENTER. The program will then be loaded.

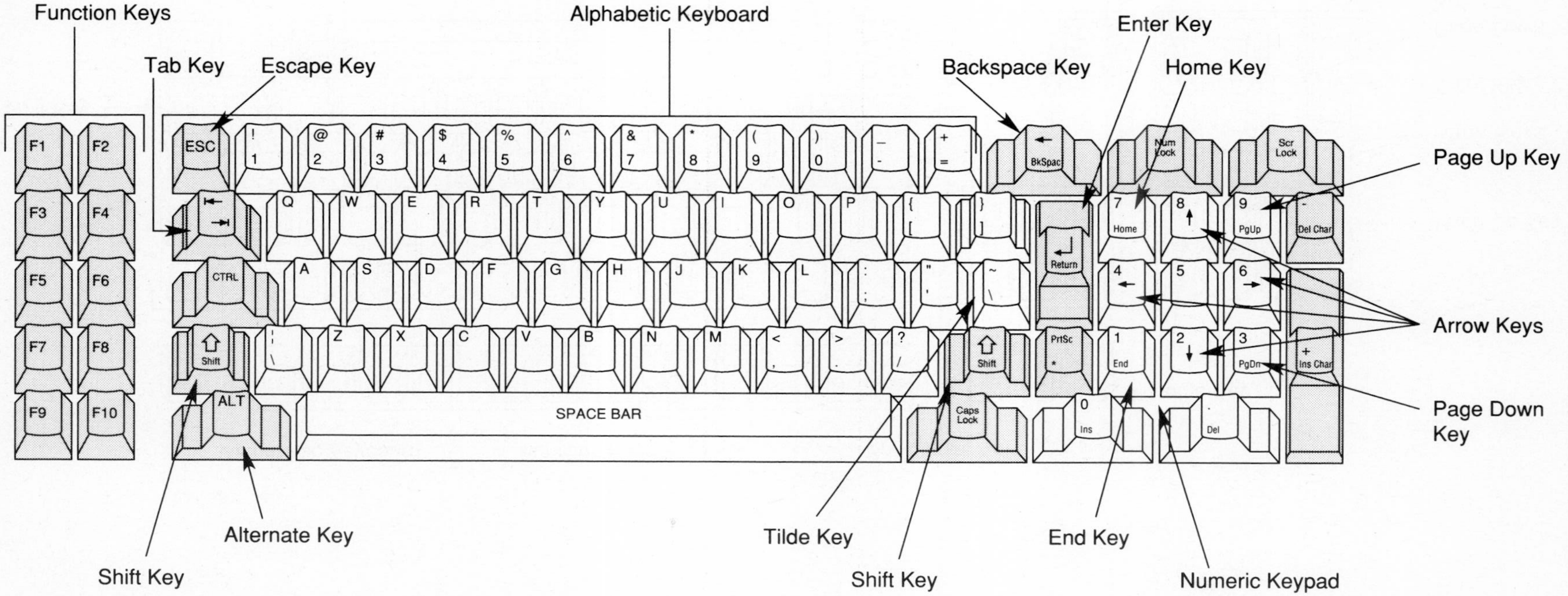

Illustration A-1 Standard IBM PC keyboard

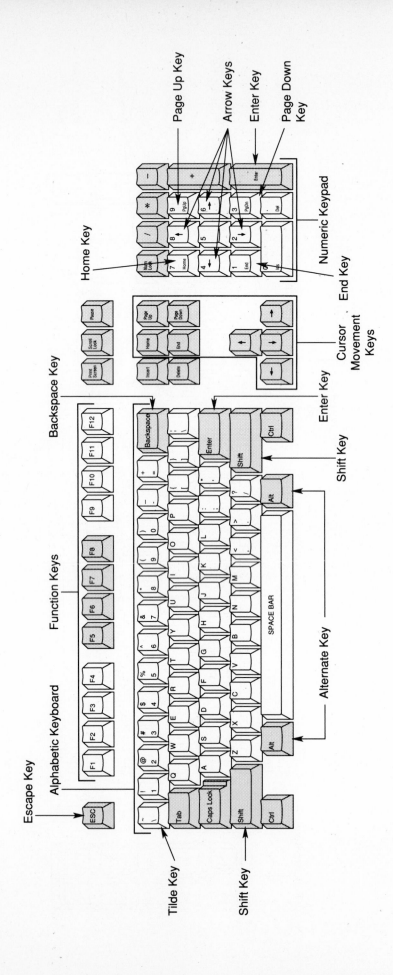

Illustration A-2 IBM XT and IBM AT keyboard

FORMATTING NEW FILE DISKS

Instead of storing models that you design on the Template Disk that accompanies this workbook, you may wish to store them on a separate disk. If you plan to store all your answer templates, you will definitely need a blank, formatted disk. It is recommended that you prepare a new disk for storing files before you begin working in Lotus 1-2-3. If you are using Version 1A of Lotus 1-2-3, you will lose your current work if you do not have a formatted disk available for storing a file.

If you have a system with two floppy disk drives, use the steps below to prepare your blank disk to store 1-2-3 files. If your system has a hard disk, follow your instructor's directions for formatting.

1. Insert an IBM PC DOS or MS DOS disk in drive A and turn the computer on.
2. At the A> prompt, type **FORMAT B:** (be sure to type the colon) and press ENTER.
3. Insert the blank disk in drive B and press ENTER.
4. When the formatting is done, press **N** in response to "Format Another?"
5. Remove the DOS disk from drive A, and insert the Template Disk that came with this workbook.
6. At the A> prompt, type **COPY INIT.PRN B:** (again, be sure to type the colon) and press ENTER.
7. When the copying is done, remove both disks and turn the computer off. Label the formatted disk as "1-2-3 File Disk."

If you are using Versions 2, 2.01, or 2.2, you do not have to exit Lotus 1-2-3 to format a disk. When you are in the Lotus 1-2-3 program, simply type **/S** (System) and then follow Steps 2 through 5 above. To return to Lotus 1-2-3, type **EXIT** at the A prompt and press ENTER.

CARE OF DISKS

Magnetic data are stored on the disk and is read by "heads" within the disk drive. Never touch the magnetic tape surfaces of the disk. Never let it get greasy, dirty, or dusty. Always handle the disk by the plastic cover only. When a disk is not in use, keep it in the paper pocket that it came in. Do not write on the disk label except with a felt-tip pen. Keep the disks away from magnetic fields such as TV screens, electric motors, etc. Disks are also sensitive to temperature extremes.

AN ASSURING NOTE

With most commercial software (programs), you do not have to worry about mistakenly touching the wrong keys on the computer. You may end up entering weird data into the computer, but this can usually be corrected by entering the proper data later. Nothing you enter will "wreck" the programs or the computer. If things get too mixed up, you can just turn off the computer and start over!

APPENDIX B

RESOLVING PROBLEMS (What to Do When Things Go Wrong)

1. I can't get a spreadsheet file to load.
   - Check to make sure that the Lotus 1-2-3 System Disk is in drive A and the Template Disk is in drive B. Files from your Template Disk will not load unless 1-2-3 is loaded first. (If you have a hard disk, make sure you have followed your instructor's directions to load Lotus 1-2-3.)
   - Check the tutorial to make sure that you are following the proper command sequence for loading files.
   - Make sure you are typing the EXACT name of the file.
   - Check the files list (/FLW and press ENTER when done) on the disk to make sure that the file you are trying to load is there.

2. I saved a file on the disk, but now it is not there.
   - You may have misspelled the file name when saving it. Check the files list on the Template Disk to make sure that the file you are trying to load is there.
   - If the file name is not in the directory, the file was not properly saved. Unfortunately, you will have to start over. An infuriating mistake when saving a file is to type /FR instead of /FS. This reloads the old file instead of saving the new one. Ouch!

3. I cannot save my file.
   - If the mode indicator shows ERROR, see Number 8 below.
   - Make sure the Template Disk is properly inserted in drive B.
   - If the computer responds with "Disk is write protected," the disk you are trying to save your file to cannot be used for saving files. A common mistake is to place a write-protect tab over the notch on the Template Disk. This should not be done because it prevents saving new files on the disk.
   - If the computer responds with "Disk full," the disk is, in fact, full. One way to solve this dilemma is to delete one or more files on the disk to make room for the new file. Erasing files will not affect the worksheet currently in the computer's memory. Type /FEW and

select the file to be deleted. Press ENTER. When the deletion is completed, type /FS to save the new file.
   - The other alternative is to use a new storage disk. If you have another disk properly formatted, simply insert that disk into drive B and save your file on it. If you do not have a disk that is formatted, you are out of luck if you are using Version 1A. You must exit the program to prepare a new disk for storage (see Appendix A or Lesson 1). If you have Versions 2, 2.01, or 2.2, type /S in the READY mode and follow the directions for formatting a disk in Appendix A or Lesson 1.

4. I can't get the printer to work right.
   - Press CTRL and BREAK keys to kill the Print command or the flashing WAIT sign.
   - You may have forgotten to enter the print range. The computer will print nothing unless the print range is specified.
   - It may be a hardware problem. Make sure the printer is connected to the computer. Make sure that the printer is turned on and that the printer is "On Line." The printer is not "On Line" if either the Line Feed (LF) or the Form Feed (FF) buttons are activated.
   - It may be a system problem. Your computer may not be sending proper messages to your printer. With some printers, special codes must be sent to the printer before it will print spreadsheet files. Consult your instructor or the 1-2-3 manual for more specific instructions.
   - If the printing is in the wrong mode (i.e., compressed, proportional spacing, etc.), turn the printer off and then turn it back on again.

5. I can't load ANY files from the Template Disk.
   - Remove the Template Disk and then reinsert it in the drive. Sometimes a disk can get out of position and needs to be reseated.
   - The disk may have been damaged, soiled, or exposed to magnetic fields or extreme temperatures. See your instructor for a replacement.

- Make sure the computer is looking to the correct drive for the file. To change the drive that Lotus 1-2-3 is reading from, type **/FD**. If the incorrect drive is specified, type the letter of the correct drive and a colon (A: or B:).

6. My printouts have unusual spacing or gaps in the middle of them.
   - Lotus 1-2-3 is preprogrammed with certain margins, borders, and page breaks. Pressing **A** (Align) before typing **G** (Go) when executing the print command should eliminate the unusual gaps. To eliminate all preprogrammed settings, type **OOUQ** (Options Other Unformatted Quit) before pressing **A**.

7. The word ERR appears on my worksheet.
   - The word ERR will appear in any cell that has a formula containing a cell address for a cell that has been deleted. Suppose that the formula in cell A18 is +F9. Suppose also that you rearrange your model and delete row 9. This will cause an ERR message in cell A18. It will also cause an ERR message in any cell with a formula that contains the cell address A18. This situation can be corrected by redoing the formula in cell A18.
   - The word ERR will appear in any cell having a formula that requires dividing one value into another but where the denominator currently has a value of zero.
   - (Version 2 only) The word ERR will appear in any cell that has a formula referencing another cell that contains a label. This is not really an error. Entering a value in the referenced cell will remove the ERR indicator. If the ERR message is annoying to you, see the Lotus 1-2-3 manual for instructions on correcting this.

8. The word ERROR appears in the mode indicator box.
   - Lotus 1-2-3 is designed to catch certain errors automatically. Check the lower left corner of the screen for a short message on the nature of the error. If you do not understand the message, you should look at the Lotus 1-2-3 Reference Manual, which contains error message explanations. Press ESC or ENTER to continue working.

9. The word CIRC appears at the bottom of the screen.
   - The word CIRC will appear if your model has a "circular reference." For example, if cell D3 has the formula +E3 and cell E3 has the formula +D3, this is a circular reference. Circular references may involve only one cell (e.g., the formula in cell E7 is +E7), two cells, or more than two cells, and it may be difficult to track down. The only way to correct a circular reference is to change the formulas in your model.

10. My worksheet loads with the cursor in a funny position.
    - When you save a spreadsheet model, the computer also saves the position of the cursor at the time the command is entered. To save the cursor in cell A1, position the cursor there by pressing the HOME key before saving the model.

11. A column of numbers does not add up.
    - This is not an error. 1-2-3 rounds numbers when displaying them on the screen. Sometimes this rounding process results in addition being off by a small amount. To correct this, use the **@ROUND** command discussed in Appendix C.

12. When I enter a decimal in a cell, the computer responds with a 0 (or a 1).
    - This is not an error. Many preprogrammed templates are designed with an integer format (**/WGFF0**). This means that decimals will be rounded. If you wish a decimal to show in a cell, format that cell to display decimals (for example, **/RFF2**) or use the General format (**/RFG**).

13. My printer won't print compressed mode (or graphics).
    - Some printers are incapable of printing in compressed mode or of printing graphics. Other printers may require special codes before compressed mode or graphics can be printed. Consult your instructor or the 1-2-3 manual for more specific instructions.

14. I can't get graphics on my screen.
    - Not all computers have graphics capabilities. Consult your instructor.

15. When I use ALT P to print my answers, "Need to run NAME file" appears where my name should be.
    - You apparently have not run the NAME file before attempting the problem. See Lesson 1 for details.

APPENDIX C
SPECIAL FUNCTION COMMANDS

Special function commands are used to perform special calculations in cells. Each function is activated by pressing the AT (@) key. Use this appendix as a reference guide as you solve the workbook problems.

Each of the following functions is used to compute a value to be entered in a cell. Functions may be linked with other standard arithmetic operations and can also be combined with one another. All of the following are legitimate 1-2-3 formulas:

    D16:+D15/@VLOOKUP(C12,E4.F9,1)
    A41:@SUM(B12.H12)+17
    A42:+A17*@IF(B1=0,2,B9)
    D18:@IF(H16>12,0,@MAX(H2.H9))

As a reminder, anytime a cell reference is used in one of these special functions, the cell reference can be entered by typing it or by using the arrow keys to "point" to the cell and then pressing ENTER.

@SUM(X.Y)

This function has already been described in Lesson 1. It is used to add numbers in a range beginning with cell X (any cell you wish) and ending with cell Y. For examples of how this function is used, refer to the tutorial and sample problems.

@SQRT(X)

This function will compute the square root of X. X can be a value or a cell reference. As a simple example, suppose you wish to compute the square root of 144 and enter the result in cell A5. Positioning the cursor in cell A5 and entering the following formula will accomplish this (remember that the cursor position is on the left followed by a colon):

    A5:@SQRT(144)

Another example is as follows:

    B8:@SQRT(A24)

In this case, you are telling 1-2-3 to take the square root of the value found in cell A24 and enter it in cell B8.

@MAX(list)

This function will return the maximum value found in a list of cells separated by commas, or in a specified range.

@MIN(list)

This function will return the minimum value found in a list of cells separated by commas, or in a specified range.

@ROUND(A,B)

This function will round the value A to the number of decimals specified by B. For example, if cell A80 contained the formula @ROUND(B71,2), the computer will round the value found in cell B71 to two decimal places and enter it in cell A80. This is different from using the **Range Format** command to format a cell to display numbers with two decimal places because the @ROUND command eliminates all values to the right of the decimal places specified. The Range Format command changes the appearance of the values on the screen but does not alter the values themselves. @ROUND(B71,0) will round the value found in cell B71 to zero decimal places (an integer).

Using this special function command would have eliminated the problem encountered in Lesson 2 (Numerical Input Errors) where a column of numbers did not add up correctly because of rounding errors.

@IF(CONDITION,A,B)

This function allows the program to choose one of two values to enter in a cell. If the specified condition is true, Value A will be put in the cell. If the condition is false, Value B will be entered. An example of how this function can be used is as follows:

    C2:@IF(A8=2,7,9)

This formula states that if the value in cell A8 is equal to 2, enter a 7 in cell C2; if the value in cell A8 is not equal to 2, enter a 9 in cell C2.

The "conditions" that may be used are as follows:

=	equal to
>	greater than
<	less than
<=	less than or equal to
>=	greater than or equal to
<>	not equal to

Here are some other acceptable examples:

B12:@IF(B11>10,B11,B10)
D23:@IF(A3<5,D8,D10/D11)
H71:@IF(G12>=0,0,@SUM(C20.C58))
F22:@IF(A1=0,B7,@IF(A1=1,B8,B9))

@VLOOKUP(A,X.Y,C) and @HLOOKUP(A,X.Y,C)

These functions allow you to look up a value in a table. They are similar in concept to the @IF function, but they allow the program to pick an answer from a whole table of values. VLOOKUP stands for a vertical table (values entered up and down), and HLOOKUP stands for a horizontal table (values entered side by side).

For an example of how the @VLOOKUP function works, suppose you are setting up a 1-2-3 model to use in tax planning for your clients. As a part of the tax planning program, you want a client's tax bracket to be automatically computed based on his/her taxable income. You obtain the following hypothetical information from the Internal Revenue Service:

Taxable Income

Over	But Not Over	Tax Bracket
$ 0	$ 5,000	15%
5,000	12,000	19
12,000	21,000	23
21,000	34,000	28
34,000	60,000	36
60,000	---	50

You can incorporate this table into your tax planning model by constructing the following table:

E40:INCOME	F40:BRACKET
E41:0.00	F41:15
E42:5000.01	F42:19
E43:12000.01	F43:23
E44:21000.01	F44:28
E45:34000.01	F45:36
E46:60000.01	F46:50

Now assume that the client's taxable income will be computed by your tax model and will be entered in cell G10. You wish to have the client's tax bracket automatically determined by the program and shown in cell G11. The following formula would be used:

G11:@VLOOKUP(G10,E41.F46,1)

The @VLOOKUP function takes the value from cell G10 and searches for a corresponding value in the income column of the table. This is called the comparison column. The search begins in cell E41 and ends when the first value greater than the value in cell G10 is found. The program then returns to the next lower value in column E, picks up the number found in the corresponding cell one column to its immediate right (the data column), and enters it in cell G11.

The range of cells entered in the middle of the @VLOOKUP formula begins with the top of the comparison column and ends with the bottom of the last data column. Lookup tables can have more than one data column. The "1" in the formula for G11 indicates that the answer is found in the first data column to the right of the comparison column.

As an example, suppose the taxable income value found in cell G10 is 10000. In evaluating cell G11, the program would jump to cell E41 and begin looking for a value greater than 10000. The first cell containing a value greater than 10000 is cell E43 (it contains 12000). The program then returns to cell E42 (the next lower value cell), picks up the corresponding value in one column to the right (19), and enters it in cell G11.

Note the following three things about the @VLOOKUP and @HLOOKUP functions:

1. If the value being searched for is less than the lowest number in the table, the program will indicate this by returning "ERR." In our example, this is what would happen if the value of G10 were less than zero.

2. The table must always be constructed in ascending order.

3. The table may be constructed in rows instead of columns. If rows are used, the @HLOOKUP function is utilized. The top row is searched (left to right) and the bottom row contains the value that is returned.

@NPV(I,X.Y)

This function will automatically compute the net present value of annual future cash flows (represented by cells X through Y) discounted at the interest rate I. The interest rate I may be expressed as a number or as a cell reference.

Suppose that an investment's projected future cash inflows at the end of each of the next three years are entered in cells D38, E38, and F38. You wish to compute the present value of these future cash flows using a discount rate of 11%. The result is to be put in cell H14. This will be accomplished by the following formula:

H14:@NPV(.11,D38.F38)

If the discount rate is found in cell B2, one of the following formulas will work:

H14:@NPV(B2,D38.F38)
or H14:@NPV(B2/100,D38.F38) if B2 is an integer

If a cash outlay is necessary at the beginning of the first year to acquire this investment, the cash outlay (found in cell G12) can be subtracted from the formula as follows:

H14:@NPV(B2,D38.F38)-G12

As with the @SUM function, when a Period (.) is entered between D38 and F38, the computer will respond with two Periods (..).

@IRR(guess,X.Y)

This function will approximate the internal rate of return for a series of cash flows (represented by cells X through Y). To start the process, you must enter an initial guess (from 0.00 to 1.0) either as a number or as a cell reference.

Suppose you wish to evaluate an investment that will cost $200,000 today and will generate $60,000 per year at the end of the first two years and $75,000 per year at the end of the next two years. The investment's projected cash flows are entered in cells B17 through B21 as follows: -$200,000; $60,000; $60,000; $75,000; and $75,000. You want the IRR to be entered in cell C6. Your initial guess is 13%. The formula is as follows:

C6:@IRR(.13,B17.B21)

If your initial guess is found in cell B3, one of the following formulas will work:

C6:@IRR(B3,B17.B21)
or C6:@IRR(B3/100,B17.B21) if B3 is an integer

@PMT(P,I,T)

This function will compute the periodic payment amount needed to pay back a loan of P dollars at an interest rate, I, over a period of time, T. T is the number of payments to be made, and I is always expressed as the interest rate per payment. For example, @PMT(100000,.11,10) would compute the annual payment needed to retire a $100,000 loan at 11% interest over ten years (the answer is $16,980.14). If the payments were to be made monthly, the formula should be written as @PMT(100000,.11/12,120) (the answer is $1,377.50). As with all other special function commands, cell references may be used in place of values anywhere in the formula.

@FV(A,I,T)

This function computes the future value of an ordinary annuity. A is the amount of the periodic payment and is assumed to occur at the end of the period. I is the interest rate per payment, and T represents the number of payments made. For example, if at the end of each year you put $100 into a savings account earning 5% interest, how much would the account be worth at the end of the fifth year? The formula @FV(100,.05,5) provides the answer ($552.56).

@PV(A,I,T)

This function computes the present value of an ordinary annuity where A is the annuity amount, I is the interest rate per payment, and T is the number of payments made. For example, @PV(100,.08,7) would compute the present value of $100 payments to be made at the end of each of the next seven years discounted at an annual rate of 8% (the answer is $520.63).

OTHER FUNCTIONS

The 1-2-3 program contains many more functions than those covered here. The ones chosen for discussion in this appendix are the most commonly used functions. You are certainly encouraged to review a more advanced 1-2-3 tutorial to learn about other functions. A partial listing of these functions is found in Appendix D of this workbook.

APPENDIX D
LOTUS 1-2-3 COMMAND SUMMARY

/COMMANDS	EXPLANATION
/WGF	Global formats for values (fixed, general, percent, etc.)
/WGL	Global label alignment (left, right, center)
/WGC	Global change of all column widths
/WGR	Global recalculation (natural, rowwise, manual, etc.)
/WGP	Turn global protection on or off
/WGD	Global default configurations
/WGZ	Global suppression of zeros (Versions 2, 2.01, and 2.2)
/WIC	Insert blank column(s)
/WIR	Insert blank row(s)
/WDC	Delete column(s)
/WDR	Delete row(s)
/WC	Set column width of current column
/WE	Erase worksheet from the screen
/WTB	Horizontal and vertical title freeze
/WTH	Horizontal title freeze
/WTV	Vertical title freeze
/WTC	Eliminate frozen titles
/WWH	Split screen horizontally (window)
/WWV	Split screen vertically (window)
/WWS	Synchronized scrolling of windows
/WWU	Unsynchronized scrolling of windows
/WWC	Eliminate split screen
/WS	Display worksheet settings
/WP	Places a page marker on worksheet for printer to use (Versions 2, 2.01, and 2.2 only)
/WL	Indicates range for recording a macro when in the LEARN mode (Version 2.2 only)
/RF	Format a cell or range of cells (fixed, general, etc.)
/RL	Label alignment for a cell or range of cells (left, right, center)
/RE	Erase a cell or range of cells
/RN	Name a cell or range of cells
/RJ	Place a written paragraph into a given range
/RP	Protect a cell or range of cells from accidental erasure or entry
/RU	Eliminate protection on a cell or range of cells
/RV	Copy the value in a cell rather than the formula (Versions 2, 2.01, and 2.2)
/RT	Transpose data from horizontal to vertical orientation or vice versa (Versions 2, 2.01, and 2.2)
/RS	Locate character strings in labels and formulas (Version 2.2)
/C	Copy a cell or range of cells
/M	Move a cell or range of cells
/FR	Retrieve (load) a file from disk
/FS	Save a file on disk
/FEW	Erase worksheet file from disk
/FL	List of files on disk
/PPR	Set range to be printed
/PPL	Line feed
/PPP	Page feed
/PPO	Printout options (header, margins, border, etc.)

/PPC	Reset printer options
/PPA	Tell 1-2-3 to begin new page at current type head position
/PPG	Print the worksheet
/PPQ	End print session; return to READY mode
/GT	Set graph type (line, bar, pie, etc.)
/GX	Set X-axis labels

/COMMANDS	EXPLANATION
/GA	Establish first data set to be displayed
/GB	Establish second data set to be displayed
/GV	View the graph on the screen
/DF	Fills a given range with sequential values
/DT	Develops a table of selected what-if results
/DS	Sorts data in ascending or descending order
/DQ	Locates data in database meeting specified criteria
/S	Exit to DOS (Versions 2, 2.01, and 2.2)
/A	Allows access to programs written by developers (Version 2.2 only)
/Q	Quit 1-2-3 session

KEYBOARD COMMANDS	EXPLANATION
F1	Help screens
F2	Edit contents of cell
F3	Select a range name from a list of all range names
F4	Establish "absolute" cell address when pointing
F5	Move cursor to specified location on worksheet
F6	Move cursor between windows
F7	Repeat most recent data query operation
F8	Select last chosen table range for data table command
F9	Force recalculation
F10	In the READY mode, redraw most recent graph
ALT-F5	Turns learn feature on and off (Version 2.2 only)
ALT-F2	Turns STEP mode on and off (Version 2.2 only)
ALT-F4	Undo feature reverses or cancels last command sequence entered (Version 2.2 only)
ESC	Cancel current entry
CTRL BREAK	Cancel current operation
←	Backspace
PG UP	Move screen up 20 lines
PG DN	Move screen down 20 lines
|←	Tab right; move screen right one page
→|	Tab left; move screen left one page (with SHIFT key)
HOME	Move cursor to cell A1
END	Use with arrow keys to move cursor to end of active area
END HOME	Move cursor to lower right corner of worksheet
NUM LOCK	Use numbers from the keypad
PRTSC	Printout of computer screen
"	Right aligned label
'	Left aligned label
^	Centered label
\	Repeating label

FUNCTION COMMANDS	EXPLANATION
@ABS(x)	Absolute value of x
@AVG(list)	Average value of list
@CHOOSE(x,a.b)	Choose xth value from list
@COS(x)	Cosine of x expressed in radians
@COUNT(list)	Count nonblank cells in list
@DATE(y,m,d)	Date
@FV(x,i,t)	Future value of an ordinary annuity
@HLOOKUP(x,a.b,y)	Look up values in a horizontal table
@IF(cond,x,y)	If condition is true, enter x; otherwise enter y
@INT(x)	Integer value of x
@IRR(x,a.b)	Internal rate of return

FUNCTION COMMANDS	EXPLANATION
@LN(x)	Natural log of x
@MAX(list)	Maximum value in list
@MIN(list)	Minimum value in list
@NPV(x,a.b)	Net present value
@PMT(p,i,t)	Payment needed to amortize investment or debt
@PV(x,i,t)	Present value of an ordinary annuity
@RAND	Random number between 0 and 1
@ROUND(x,n)	Round the value x to n decimal places
@SQRT(x)	Square root of value x
@STD(list)	Standard deviation of list values
@SUM(list)	Sum of list of values
@VLOOKUP(x,a.b,y)	Look up value x in a vertical table

INDEX